SOMNIQUEST

SOMNIQUEST

the 5 types of sleeplessness and how to overcome them

**Alice Kuhn Schwartz, PhD
and Norma S. Aaron**

HARMONY BOOKS
New York

To all of you who last night turned and tossed restlessly in your beds, this book is dedicated—with the reminder that in your search for sleep you are assisted by all the research scientists who investigate the dimensions of sleep behavior, and by your own natural ability to sleep, which, having lost, you can regain.

Designed by Rebecca Schiffrin

Published simultaneously in Canada by General Publishing Co., Ltd.
Printed in the United States of America

Library of Congress Cataloging in Publication Data

Schwartz, Alice K
    Somniquest.
    Includes bibliographical references and index.
    1. Insomnia. I. Aaron, Norma S., joint author
II. Title. [DNLM: 1. Insomnia—Popular works. WM188 S399s]
RC548.S35 1979   616.8'49   78-27594
ISBN 0-517-53698-6

Contents

The Somniquest System grew out of the authors' personal struggles with sleeplessness. The conquest of their own insomnias led to the formulation of the program on a theoretical basis. It was subsequently administered as both individual and group therapy to men and women whose discontent impelled them to seek professional help. Clinical results confirmed the effectiveness of the method in the alleviation and prevention of insomnia.

Anxiety Antidotes

Little-Known Facts about Sleep

1. Many healthy and vigorous people sleep for as little as four hours each night.

2. Experimental subjects tested after sleep deprivation were capable of performing difficult tasks.

3. Neither heart attacks, nor strokes, nor cancer, nor any other serious ailments have been consistently associated with lack of sleep.

4. There is little evidence to link hours of sleep per night with life expectancy.

5. Lack of sleep does not cause a lined and haggard face, or dark rings under the eyes.

6. Wide individual differences in the need for sleep may be observed even in neonatal infants. Many people require far less sleep than they believe.

7. Natural compensation insures that a night of poor sleep will be followed by one or more nights of longer sleep, usually within a two-week period. Most people average the same amount of sleep within every two-week period.

8. At college age, half the population of the United States sleep less than eight hours per night, and after college age half the population sleep less than seven hours per night.

9. Experimental subjects who submitted to prolonged periods of sleep deprivation required a relatively short amount of sleep to recoup their loss.

10. During the past thirty years the average amount of sleep for individuals in the United States has decreased, while at the same time life expectancy has increased.

11. Wakefulness in time of stress is an adaptive survival mechanism and the mark of a healthy person.

Personal Sleep Profile

Questionnaire and Answers

If you are a victim of insomnia, first answer this questionnaire. You may identify more than one type of insomnia in yourself; this is not uncommon. Then check your answers against those noted on the pages which follow. Your answers will supply the term which most closely describes your type of insomnia. They will enable you to reach a self-diagnosis. Your diagnosis, however, is tentative. As you read, you may encounter information which will lead you to modify or to change your self-evaluation.

1. How many hours of sleep per night do you average?
   If your answer is less than five hours, you are suffering scurzomnia.

2. How many hours of sleep per night do you need to feel rested?
   If your answer is eight or more hours, your problem lies in the quality rather than the quantity of your sleep.

3. How long does it take you to fall asleep?
   If your answer is thirty minutes or more hours, you are suffering initardia.

4. How many times do you awaken during the night?
   If your answer is three or more, you are suffering pleisomnia.

5. How long have you had insomnia?
   If your answer is less than six months, you may be experiencing a transitory condition. If your answer is more than six months, you have acquired poor sleep habits which require correction.

6. Do you lie in bed awake for long periods of time?
   If yes, you are probably suffering hyperlixia compounded by poor sleep habits.

7. Are you frequently troubled by unpleasant dreams?
   If yes, you are suffering turbula.

8. Do you have frequent nightmares?
   If yes, you are suffering turbula.

9. Does any other member of your immediate family suffer from insomnia?
   If yes, you have a predisposition to insomnia.

10. Were you a poor sleeper in infancy, childhood, or during adolescence?
    If yes, you have a predisposition to insomnia.

11. Did your sleep problems begin after an unhappy experience?
    If yes, your sleep problem may be covering underlying anger.

12. Are you often depressed?
    If yes, your sleep problem may be covering underlying anger.

13. Do you go to bed at widely different hours?
    If yes, you are suffering mini-jet-lag.

14. Do you nap during the day?
    If yes, you are overdrawing your sleep account.

15. Do you sleep late on weekend mornings?
    If yes, you are probably suffering Sunday night insomnia.

16. Is your bedroom within earshot of intermittent noises, such as a firehouse or railroad train?
    If yes, the noise may be interfering with the natural sleep stage progression.

17. Have you been told that you snore loudly and irregularly?
    If yes, you must investigate the possiblilty of sleep apnea.

18. Do you thrash, toss, and turn in your sleep?
    If yes, you must investigate the possibility of sleep apnea.

19. Do you take sleep-inducing medication regularly?
    If yes, you are suffering drug-related insomnia.

20. Do you review the events of the day when you get into bed at night?

If yes, you have acquired poor sleep habits which require correction.

21. Do you plan your activities for the following day when you get into bed?

    If yes, you have acquired poor sleep habits which require correction.

22. Do you awaken with a start, feeling completely alert at once?

    If yes, you may be suffering from an unconscious fear which is interfering with your ability to sleep.

23. Do you read, watch television, eat, or make telephone calls while in bed?

    If yes, you have acquired habits which compete with sleep.

24. Does your husband, wife, child, friend, or lover sympathize with your inability to sleep?

    If yes, you may be reaping secondary gain from your inability to sleep.

CHAPTER 1

The Somniquest System

When you lie awake in the middle of the night, it must seem to you that everyone else in the world is asleep. Your telephone is silent. You hear only an occasional automobile passing on the street. You hear no footsteps, no voices, no dogs barking, no doorbells ringing, no water gurgling in the pipes, no elevators stopping in the hall outside your door. You are alone, you feel abandoned. The stillness generates a sense of uneasiness, sometimes even fright.

The next time you waken, remember that actually you are not alone. One out of every seven adults in this country suffers from one or more of the categories of insomnia: *initardia, pleisomnia, scurzomnia, hyperlixia, turbula, multisomnia.* Many even suffer *all* these insomnias at different times—they are the victims of *pansomnia.* And so when you turn on your light to look at the clock, remember that millions of other little lights are blinking in every town and city in this country. Sleep difficulties are so widespread that one out of every two adults has swallowed a tranquilizer or sleep drug at some time. In this country, thirty million people have lost the habit of sleep. If you are one of those afflicted thirty million, this book is designed to teach you how to recover the ability with which every newborn infant is endowed. We will disclose the precise steps you must take to rediscover the art of falling and staying asleep.

What is insomnia? How can it be defined? Not by number of hours of sleep. One person sleeping six hours per night may feel perfectly comfortable. Another may be miserable, tired, jittery, cranky. We have defined insomnia as stressful wakefulness that leaves the victim tired and uncomfortable. Put another way, it is sleep of such poor quality and such limited quantity that the sleeper is uncomfortable and unable to function efficiently the following day.

It has been pointed out that no one ever died of insomnia. Undoubtedly so, but that observation is likely to prove more of an irritant than a comfort. Equally irritating is the term *pseudoinsomnia* employed by sleep laboratories. We find the label offensive. If you are unable to sleep, there is nothing "pseudo" about it. The results are painfully real. Some of our participants became depressed every night as bedtime approached. An attractive young woman with long blond hair and big gray eyes joined us after she had separated from her boyfriend. He had lost patience with her inability to enjoy herself when she was feeling exhausted for want of sleep week after week. Several married couples had lost the comfortable intimacy of a shared bedroom, because one or both were too easily awakened and unable to fall back to sleep. One man reported, "I always start the day wrong because I can't smile in the morning."

Although we speak of insomnia as a single entity, actually it assumes several forms, each requiring a different, specific treatment. We have devised our own classification.

1. hyperlixia (Greek, *hyper*, excessive; Middle English, *liht*, light): excessively light sleep. This kind of sleep falls between sleep and wakefulness. In our surveys, light sleep is the least frequently mentioned complaint, but actually it is more prevalent than is realized by nonsleepers. It probably underlies most of the other complaints.

2. initardia (Latin, *initium*, a beginning): the inability to initiate sleep, to fall asleep in the first instance. This is often found in people aged twenty to thirty.

3. pleisomnia (Indo-European, *plei*, to split or crack): broken sleep characterized by frequent awakenings.

4. scurzomnia (Old High German, *scurz*, short): short sleep. The victim may fall asleep easily and sleep well, but within a few hours awakens completely and is unable to fall back to sleep for the balance of the night.

5. turbula (Latin, *turbare,* to trouble): troubled sleep. This is characterized by frequent nightmares and uneasy feelings. Sleep assumes an unpleasant tone, so much so that the victim dreads going to sleep. Turbula usually appears in response to an unhappy life event. We have all suffered turbula in times of stress, but with some unfortunates it persists, terrorizing them night after night. This type of insomnia is thought by many to be fairly infrequent, but in our practice we have encountered so many cases that we believe the frequency has been underestimated.

The five insomnias often join in various combinations called *multisomnia*, which is any combination of two or more of the five, such as initardia plus hyperlixia, or pleisomnia plus turbula, or any other grouping of the five. Finally, while it is impossible to experience all five of the insomnias at the same time, some unfortunates have suffered all of them at different times. Our term for this is *pansomnia*. Poor sleep usually asserts itself in several forms, either during the same period of time or during successive periods. Most poor sleepers find themselves contending with a capricious set of symptoms that supplant each other with surprising fluidity. Acquainting yourself with all of the forms of insomnia will enable you to take preventive as well as remedial measures.

Almost every adult has experienced some sleepless nights. In most instances, the condition clears up shortly. In some, however, it persists. We have observed that once insomnia takes hold, the victim unwittingly aggravates, and then perpetuates, the condition. There are any number of ways to perpetuate insomnia. The participants in the Somniquest program, in attempting to find comfort, all inadvertently prolonged their distress. They all made mistakes.

Mistake #1

Selma, a secretary, found herself forced to live with an unhappy family situation. She was aware that there was nothing that she could do or say to change the situation. Night after night, she rehearsed in her mind the things she would like to say if she were free to talk. She became so agitated that she was unable to sleep. Naturally, she felt more and more exhausted as days, weeks, and months passed. Finally, she decided that the next best thing to sleeping would be to lie quietly in bed. Every night she went to bed at 11:00 P.M. and did not leave her bed until 7:30 in the morning, no matter how briefly she had slept.

Mistake #2

Blanche, a charming, attractive Englishwoman who arrived in this country when she was sixteen, recently retired. She had been employed as a statistician for an insurance company. In retirement, with little physical, intellectual, or social stimulation, there was nothing to fatigue her at the end of the day. She suffered an onset of hyperlixia combined with scurzomnia, awakening each night after only a few hours of sleep. She had read somewhere that cheese and milk are foods for sleep. Every 4:00 A.M., when she awakened, she put on her robe, padded to the refrigerator, ate a snack of imported cheese and drank a glass of milk.

Mistake #3

Toby, an intelligent, well-read matron, maintained two homes, one in the United States and another in the Caribbean. She generally kept herself occupied with many activities. Nevertheless, she found herself either unable to fall asleep (initardia) or waking frequently in the middle of the night (pleisomnia). She was far too active a person to lie still, and so she would tiptoe into the den in order not to disturb her husband, and then she would either listen to a radio talk show or watch a late late television movie.

Mistake #4

Thelma, a writer, suffered a severe trauma when her father died. She was later shown a copy of his will, naming her as principal beneficiary of his estate. Her mother, the executrix of the estate, took possession of the funds and refused to turn them over to Thelma. She was faced with the painful decision of whether or not to take her mother to court. When she decided against legal action, she found herself tossing and turning in bed every night, unable to sleep. In order to take her mind off her outrage and frustration, she developed the habit of writing during the night until she was exhausted, usually about 3:00 A.M., after which she would sleep until noon the following day.

Mistake #5

Rachel, a stunning woman in her forties, owned a fashionable boutique. Born in Germany, she was imprisoned in Auschwitz at the age of sixteen. The prospect of imminent death had made sleep fearful while she was there. Now, almost thirty years later, sleep was still synonymous with death. In order to insure a restful night, she would get into a comfortable old flannel nightgown early in the evening, draw the window shades so that no light could seep into the room, and lie still in bed.

All five mistakes were attempts at self-comfort. They seem innocuous enough. However, the very steps taken for comfort in fact produced a habit of insomnia.

You may be thinking, "But what about me? Nothing dramatic ever happened to me. I wasn't in a concentration camp. My arguments with my mother never went beyond hurt feelings. Why did my sleep problems begin?" Most people do not suffer a traumatic onset. Insomnia can start from something as unremarkable as an uncomfortable mattress. Unless we have back trouble, we tend to give very little thought to the mattress on which we spend some 30 percent of our lives. Some people expect one mattress to last a lifetime. They even neglect to turn it regularly so that, in time, hollows develop, causing movement during sleep to be difficult, which results in minor discomfort. To a deep sleeper, this doesn't matter, but to a light sleeper the slight discomfort may make the difference. A restless bed partner who flings his arms, or turns over frequently, can disrupt his partner's slow descent into restful sleep. Minor aches and pains, the kind you barely notice, can keep you awake. There are dozens of almost subliminal nagging conditions that may be bothering you—aching muscles and joints, sinus pains, digestive upsets, old surgical wounds, and the like.

Another determinant, one that we often encounter in college students, involves irregularity in sleep hours. We all operate on what is called a *circadian* (*circa,* about; *diem,* a day) *rhythm*. The body obeys a cycle of about twenty-four hours' duration. Within each twenty-four-hour period, temperature, pulse rate, and other body functions, including sleep, fluctuate according to the time of day or night. If you were to remain in an isolated room without daylight or clocks, and eat and sleep at will, you would still function on a close to twenty-four-hour schedule. You would automatically regulate your activities by reference to a figurative internal time clock. Irregular sleep intervals tend to disrupt this internal circadian clock. When you go to bed at widely different hours you are creating a simulated jet lag, and so you are affecting your sleep behavior. Although regularity in sleep hours is not, by itself, sufficient to cure insomnia, nevertheless the opposite factor, that is to say *irregularity* in sleep hours, is often sufficient to precipitate insomnia by jarring your internal clock.

Still another precipitant is depression. Depression goes hand in hand with lethargy. It kills enthusiasm. It inhibits muscle activity. If you doubt this, think how difficult it is to squeeze your facial muscles into a smile when you are dejected. Try to jump rope when you are gloomy—you will not succeed. One would imagine that depression ought to lead to increased sleep. Sometimes it does, but more often it does not. Underneath most depression there lies a turbulent, boiling pool of anger. Depression is anger turned inward. Depressed people are usually gentle, kind souls who do not strike out in anger. They do not habitually shout, scream, or curse, or if occasionally they do, they feel intensely guilty about their behavior. Nevertheless, they suffer anger like everybody else; they simply take their seething rage and hold it down inside, often unaware they are doing this. The anger then emerges as depression.

These people frequently treat others with more kindness than they extend to themselves. They rake themselves over hot coals for every mistake. One man told us that if other people spoke to him the way he speaks to himself, he would never talk to them again. He is typical of a specific kind of personality, lenient with others and strict with himself to the point of demanding perfection. These are the people who tend to develop insomnia.

This personality factor emerged time and time again as we listened to the men and women who had developed sleep difficulties. When a new participant complained of insomnia, we would ask for a precise description of the problem, and then we would ask, if the person was married, "What about your husband [or wife]?"

Usually, the answer was "He sleeps like a top," or "She falls asleep the minute her head touches the pillow, and needs an alarm to wake her." There seem to be only two kinds of people, those who cannot sleep and those who cannot stay awake, and we had the impression that they always marry each other.

The next question we would ask was "How do you feel when you are lying awake and you look at your partner sleeping peacefully?"

Our participants invariably denied any resentment or annoyance. The denial furnishes the clue to this aspect of the personality of the insomniac. Remember, it is natural to resent the other fellow when he or she has what you want. It may not be reasonable, but it is a normal reaction. Remember, too, that emotions do not reason; they react. Nevertheless, most victims of insomnia find it necessary to reject their unacceptable feelings. Some of them do so consciously, while others behave unconsciously by repressing the feelings entirely. Thus, the insomniac personality may be described as one that needs to deny, either consciously or unconsciously, feelings of hostility toward important people in his or her life. To put it another way, the non-sleeper is often a perfectionist who makes impossible self-demands.

If the description fits you, you should not conclude that your personality produced your insomnia. It simply made you vulnerable. At the same time, you must realize that you are enduring intense self-punishment. It is a good idea to take stock. It might help you to be kind to yourself as well as to others. Try it.

Although the idea may surprise you, insomnia is a habit. It is a habit like nail-biting, smoking, gambling, or overeating. The attempt to conquer insomnia is nothing more nor less than the attempt to break a bad habit. It is customary, of course, to classify only voluntary acts, such as gambling and drinking, as habits. Insomnia, on the other hand, is largely involuntary. However, studies have shown that involuntary behavior is subject to the same control as voluntary behavior, so that insomnia, a habit, can be broken just as other habits are broken. Before we go any further, a subsidiary point must be made. Sleep, a complex form of behavior, is not purely involuntary. If it were, you might fall asleep while driving your automobile, while swimming, or in the midst of an introduction to Robert Redford or Farrah Fawcett-

Majors. Sleep is supported by many voluntary actions, like lying down, lounging in a comfortable chair, relaxing, or even just making a decision to sleep. Have you ever remained in bed for a length of time, during an illness, perhaps? Do you recall saying to yourself at some point, "I think I'll go to sleep," and then turning over and sleeping? You made a decision to sleep before you slept. We can see then that sleep includes voluntary as well as involuntary components, and that, as forms of habitual behavior, both are subject to your control.

The Somniquest System employs the methods that have proven to be most effective in breaking habits. Somniquest draws upon the work of Pavlov, Skinner, Hull, Guthrie, Tolman, and additionally upon the works of others, including Rogers, Maslow, and to some extent, Sigmund Freud and the theorists who elaborated his formulations.

In addition to an effort to alter your habits, Somniquest attempts to change your attitude as well. The effect of attitude upon sleep is powerful. We will therefore, in the following chapters, supply you with relevant information regarding your need for sleep, and the effects of shortened sleep upon health. When you are thoroughly acquainted with all of the available data regarding lack of sleep, your attitude may undergo reversal.

One of our participants, Ezra, said in a published interview, "I used to go to bed expecting to stay awake, and I did. Now I expect to sleep all night, and I do." Ezra was saying that his changed attitude had produced a change, for the better, in his sleep. One woman in her sixties, the victim of a mild heart attack, informed us that her physician had literally ordered her to sleep. "It is most important for your health," he insisted. "You must sleep eight hours. If you can't," he added, "I want you to take this pill," whereupon he handed her a prescription for Valium. Needless to say, with fright as a background, the woman did not sleep for eight hours a night either with or without the drug. This worried woman is not an isolated case. Many people have consulted us concerned that an inadequate amount of sleep is injurious to their health. Unfortunately, their anxiety itself interferes with their ability to sleep. Attitude and expectation exert a stronger influence on the body than we realize. Body mechanisms can be set in action by our very thoughts. Worry, anger, the expectation of being unable to fall asleep, your anxiety about your failure to sleep, all will activate physical responses that will interfere with your ability to sleep well. Therefore, you will need to change your attitude toward sleep as well as your sleep habits. A degree of change will occur automatically as you learn more about your need for sleep. In addition, you may elect to employ the techniques of attitude change that will be explained in detail in the appropriate chapters.

In Somniquest, we start with an assumption of health. We do not look for illness; we treat problems. We seek out your strengths and your vitality, and we work with those qualities. We believe that every human being has a natural drive toward health, that every person will find a better way to live if offered guidance and encouragement. Of course, we do recognize that in a small percentage of cases insomnia accompanies physical or emotional difficulties of a serious nature. Almost every adult has experienced sleeplessness at one time or another. Some of these attacks are occasioned by a life event. Other episodes are physical in origin. It is important to treat physical factors before employing the Somniquest System. An examination by a physician to rule out or to treat physical first causes is recommended.

The Somniant Techniques, presleep exercises to help you sleep, are described on pages 193–204. They are designed to be used one at a time, with each to be practiced every night for one full week. Start with *The Sleep Swing.* Practice this technique for seven consecutive nights. Then, at the beginning of the second week, learn *The Sleep Stretch,* to be similarly practiced for seven consecutive nights. Continue in this fashion until you have mastered all of the Somniant Techniques. At the end of seven weeks, when you have afforded each of them an adequate trial, you will be able to judge which is best for you in the event that a sleepless episode occurs in the future.

It is important to appreciate that we are not suggesting any magical cures. You cannot cure insomnia by taking a pill. You cannot cure insomnia by taking a hundred pills. Similarly, you cannot cure insomnia by reading a book as you would take a pill. Remember, you developed your own insomnia as a habit and an attitude. If the condition is sufficiently distressful to make you willing to put in a lot of hard work in the opposite direction, this book will tell you precisely how to eliminate your insomnia. The road is hard and difficult to travel, but we hold your hand and guide you every step of the way.

General Prescripts and Proscripts for Restful Sleep

In order to replace unsatisfactory sleep with an adequate quantity of restful, pleasant sleep, you must follow our directives, the prescripts and proscripts that are listed at the end of each chapter. They will instruct you in the procedures necessary to create in yourself a receptivity to sleep, an invitation which sleep will accept. The following general directives apply in all cases.

• Do nothing in bed but sleep. Only sex is excluded from this proscript—more about sex later. We are constantly amazed at the variety of activities that are conducted in bed. Eating, drinking, watching television, reading, and telephoning are among the more common activities in bed. Others include manicuring, sewing, bookkeeping, letter writing, and knitting. If you do anything in bed but sleep, you must stop now for all time. Your aim is to strengthen the association between bed and sleep, so that bed automatically elicits sleep. In order to accomplish this, all other associations to bed must be eliminated.

This basic rule is based on solid psychological principles. When faced with a familiar situation, we tend to behave in the same manner we behaved before in that situation. Haven't you ever met someone on the street and answered their greeting with "Fine," only to realize a moment later that the greeting was not "How are you?" Have you ever passed a building where once you had an emotional experience and felt the same emotion again, even before you recalled the experience? You were repeating a response to a stimulus. Jack Benny, the comedian, made excellent use of this principle. Everybody had seen him. When he appeared on the stage, he would simply stand there deadpan, looking straight ahead or from one side to another. Slowly, laughter would ripple, then swell over the audience. His viewers were laughing because when they had last seen him, they had laughed. Jack Benny was the stimulus, laughter was the automatic response.

Analogously, your bed is the stimulus, and sleep should be the response. If you have engaged in other activities in bed, bed as the stimulus will evoke all of those other responses in addition to sleep. If you have eaten, read, watched television, your taste buds, your imagination, and your alertness system will all become aroused when you get into bed and will compete with your sleep response. More often than not, a response other than sleep will win the competition and thus prevent you from sleeping. Therefore, you must do nothing in bed but sleep. This proscript is critical for sleep improvement. It will take some time before you feel the effect, but don't give up. As you continue to eliminate all other responses, they will slowly be extinguished. Most of our participants reported substantial improvement within a period of three weeks.

• Never remain in bed, awake, for more than thirty minutes. Keep a clock with a lighted dial in your bedroom. Look at the clock when you go to bed and when you awaken during the night. If you are still awake after thirty minutes, get out of bed. This is essential, because every minute that you lie in bed while awake subtracts itself from sleep time. EEG (electroencephalogram) studies have shown that when you toss and turn in bed you are actually drifting in and out of light sleep. All of your uncomfortable minutes or hours are substituting for deep, restful sleep. In addition, by permitting this to occur, you are acquiring a case of habitual hyperlixia (see Chapter Four). Don't ever deceive yourself that you are up all night in bed. If you're lying down, you're not up. If you're really awake, get out of bed.

Everyone awakens momentarily from time to time during the night. These waking moments are revealed in EEG records. Poor sleepers are completely unaware of their sleep periods between the waking moments, and aware only of wakefulness. It has been found, oddly enough, that your thought processes continue while you are sleeping lightly. One of your recurrent thoughts during light sleep is the thought that you are awake. Sometimes, during sleep counseling, when our participants tried to get out of bed, they were literally unable to do so. This indicates that they were actually in light sleep. Their muscles were too relaxed to allow them to get up. If this should happen to you, simply say silently, "I'm really asleep." Your statement will banish the dreamlike thought and you will descend into a deeper, more comfortable phase. But, by all means, try to get out of bed. If you are awake, you will succeed.

• When you get out of bed during the night, do something boring. Do not eat, or drink, or read a good book, or watch an old movie. If you do something that is pleasurable, you will strengthen your awakening habit. If you eat ice cream, for example, you will awaken for ice cream on other nights.

Experimental evidence clearly demonstrates that "satisfyers" solidify habits. Any response that is followed by a satisfyer, also called a reward, such as food, drink, praise, or pleasure of any kind, will be repeated. If awakening during the night has already become a habit, a pleasure that follows the awakening will strengthen your habit. This type of habit formation has been shown to be true of animals, children, and adults, whether or not they are aware of why they repeat the rewarded response. Think of waking up during the night as a response. Be careful not to follow it with a reward.

• Of course, once you are out of bed, you must do something. We suggest that you read a textbook, or any other nonstimulating material, learn the metric system, do crossword puzzles, play solitaire. Any repetitive, eye-tiring task, such as needlepoint, is also good. One of our participants conjugated irregular French verbs to improve her language skill. You can probably think of a number of other quiet, soporific tasks for yourself.

• Go back to bed when you reach the point of sleep readiness that is indicated in the Back-to-Bed Guide.

• Keep a warm body, a cool room. Make sure that your body is comfortably warm when you get into bed. Wear bed socks in the winter if your feet get cold. Discomfort signals from the body to the brain act like sirens to disturb the sleep centers. Unless your bedroom is already quite cold, lower your bedroom temperature. You will find that you sleep more deeply in a cool room.

• Sex is recommended whenever, wherever, and with whomever you choose. It alleviates tension. It is a powerful soporific. And what is more, it's fun. Enjoyment, good health, wide interests, all create the background for peaceful sleep. The road to sleep branches into other byways. Explore all of them.

In summary:
- Do nothing in bed but sleep.
- After thirty minutes of wakefulness, get out of bed.
- When you get out of bed during the night, do something that you find boring.
- Return to bed only when you feel sleepy.
- Do not eat, drink, or engage in other pleasurable activities during nighttime awakenings.
- Keep a warm body, a cool bedroom.
- Sexual activity is excepted from all blanket prohibitions. Sex is recommended as a general soporific.
- Practice a Somniant Technique (pp. 193-204) immediately upon retiring, or immediately after awakening during the night.

CHAPTER 2
Initardia

Initardia is the inability to fall asleep—the inability to *initiate* sleep promptly. It is the most common form of insomnia. Unlike most of the other insomnias, it often strikes early in life, finding victims in their thirties, twenties, and even younger. Whenever a young person complained to us of insomnia, we were fairly certain that the complaint was initardia. The youngest insomniac we ever treated, Denise, was a twelve-year-old girl who suffered initardia.

Initardia has recently assumed epidemic proportions, especially among men and women in the glamor professions of television, publishing, and fashion, as well as among single people in all types of work. We attribute the unprecedented increase to current life styles, which, for the general population, have changed substantially in the past fifteen years. Instead of dining at 6:30 or 7:00 P.M. it is now fashionable to arrive at the popular restaurants at 8:30, and the favorite dining rooms in the big cities blaze alive between 9:30 and 10:00 P.M. At some of the restaurants, the sound levels, at this hour, approach the pain threshold, and the air pulsates with excitement. It is easy to understand that a few hours of testing your personal magnetism in this charged atmosphere is not likely to send you home lulled into drowsy relaxation.

When you stay out late on some nights, and then go to bed early on other nights, you create your own mini-jet-lag, with the adjustment problems which invariably accompany the jet-lag experience. Comparison of poor sleepers and good sleepers reveals one factor that is shared by many good sleepers and few poor sleepers: regular hours! This statistic should not be taken to mean that a fixed nightly bedtime will, by itself, induce good sleep. Actually, it is of no significant assistance in the initiation of sleep, but bedtime regularity will certainly help to maintain good sleep once the sleep habit itself has been established. However, we are not advocating the sacrifice of your social life in the interest of sleep; sleep is a road to personal comfort, not an end in itself. We will teach you to initiate sleep at widely different hours through the use of Somniant Techniques, a presleep ritual, and healthy sleep habits.

Overstimulation and mini-jet-lag are only part of the initardia picture. For some people, getting into bed is a signal to worry. They immediately map out their activities for the following day, marking caution spots and danger zones. Planning of this nature precipitates an accelerated heart rate, an irregular breathing rate, and other autonomic responses sharply antagonistic to sleep. The other side of this rehearsal coin is a review of the day just ended. Even those of us who do not spend hours brooding have, at one time or another, used the presleep period to reexamine the events of the day, and to experience again that day's emotions. Some initardiacs routinely use this time to stir up their emotions, rather than to allow them to rest.

Physiologically, it is impossible to fall asleep while you are upset or excited. You must calm down first. Your body is incapable of supporting both arousal and sleep simultaneously. The sympathetic nervous system concerns itself with stress reactions, or what have been termed the fight-or-flight responses. Fear, anger, worry, or any other strong emotion galvanizes the sympathetic nervous system into action. When the sympathetic system is activated, the parasympathetic nervous system, which governs such vegetative responses as digestion and sleep, is inhibited. If you make a habit of worrying, and thus turning on your sympathetic nervous system, each time you turn off the light to prepare for sleep, you will need to retrain yourself to work with your body, instead of against it. You will need to stop turning on your sympathetic nervous system with worry, rehearsal, or review of emotion-laden events. You must give your timid subsystem, the parasympathetic, a chance to take over. Practice the Somniant Techniques, which are designed for this purpose.

Sometimes a sleep problem is mistakenly diagnosed as initardia. People frequently overestimate the amount of time it takes to fall asleep. Studies in sleep laboratories often uncover errors in time estimation. In these hospital laboratories, patients must be prepared, at bedtime, for electrical brain wave readings. Wires are pasted to the eyes, temples, and the top of the head, and then the wires are drawn back into a sort of pony tail. In addition, a tiny thermometer may be inserted into the rectum to remain there all night, or, in some cases, special equipment may draw samples of blood during the night. The wires are connected to a control board located at the head of the bed. Some laboratories include, mounted near the ceiling, a closed-circuit television camera. In others a one-way mirror is installed. The patient, or experimental subject, is put to bed, in a strange bed, in a strange place, in the presence of strangers, with the knowledge that every breath, every movement is under observation. Would you fall asleep under those conditions? It seems inconceivable that anyone could or would fall asleep in that situation. Nevertheless, it usually takes no more than ten or fifteen minutes before the subject falls asleep. The individuals who fall asleep so quickly are likely to estimate a much longer time period before the onset of their sleep. Time estimation in sleep-wake situations is often grossly inaccurate. The prescripts and proscripts at the end of this chapter will help you to estimate accurately the actual time it takes you to fall asleep. If it takes as much as thirty minutes, you are suffering initardia, which, fortunately, is a comparatively docile form of insomnia. It will yield to persistent retraining in a matter of weeks.

If you are convinced that you are actually lying awake for a long period, but at the same time you cannot literally prove that you have been awake, either by a written notation or by any other objective evidence, then there is every indication that, although you feel you were awake, you were actually sleeping, albeit lightly. Paradoxical as it may seem, it is a common phenomenon among insomniacs to sleep lightly and to have a clear recollection that they were not asleep at all, but actually awake. Some of the sleep laboratories call this phenomenon "pseudoinsomnia." In view of the proven distress that this light sleep produces, so far as we are concerned there is nothing "pseudo" about it. It is real—it is actual—it is, in fact, hyperlixia. The light, uneasy sleep of hyperlixia is easily confused with wakefulness. Therefore, you must pay special attention to the chapter on hyperlixia. There we will explain how to hasten your descent from light sleep into a deeper, more restful sleep.

Initardia is often supported by an intriguing mechanism, the self-fulfilling prophecy, in which the mere prediction of certain events increases the probability of these events. The self-fulfilling prophecy is one of the peculiar side effects of preelection polls. As soon as a poll finds one of several candidates to be a favorite, hundreds, sometimes thousands, of voters jump on the band-wagon to make the candidate even more of a favorite. In a comparable manner, should you prophesy that you will make a positive impression in a work-related situation, the odds are that you will then reflect the self-confidence best calculated to create a favorable impact. Similarly, if you expect that you will not sleep tonight, that very expectation will operate to keep you awake. Once you have fallen asleep quickly several times, your negative expectation will naturally undergo reversal. However, if you are at all suggestible, we may be able to shake up your self-fulfilling prophecy right now.

Are you, in fact, suggestible? (Incidentally, suggestibility reflects neither intelligence nor lack of intelligence. It is a neutral characteristic. To be suggestible is simply to be responsive.) If you do not know whether you are suggestible, try this test. Do you find aspirin to be effective most of the time? If your answer is yes, you are probably at least slightly suggestible. It has been established that a significant percent of the aspirin remedy involves a placebo effect, which is to say the same effect would occur if you had taken a sugar pill. Consequently, if you have found aspirin to be of help most of the time, you are working with an excellent subject—yourself. And so try saying to yourself, and say it aloud, "I will fall asleep more quickly tonight." You may not believe this statement. No matter. Say it aloud anyway. Now, count to ten and say it again, silently this time. That is all. You have immediately weakened your negative expectation. You have used the technique of autosuggestion.

During the baseball season, the American public is treated to remarkable displays of autosuggestion. Mark Fidrych, a pitcher for the Detroit Tigers, renders a vivid demonstration of autosuggestion at its best each time he prepares to pitch the ball. He is known as the Bird. Before the Bird winds up, he looks the ball straight in its hypothetical eye and talks to it. He tells that ball, in no uncertain terms, the precise path and the exact velocity he wishes it to take. More often than not, the ball obeys. Now you and I know that the ball hasn't heard a word. Well then, who heard? The Bird heard! Autosuggestion. It works for Mark. It can also work for you. It can destroy your negative self-fulfilling prophecy.

When Denise, our youngest patient, felt that she would not fall asleep, her negative expectation resulted in panic for her and a sleepless night for the rest of her family. Denise was only twelve years old, with many problems, including the problem of sleep. Her parents suspected that something was amiss when, as a two-year-old, Denise flew into severe tantrums at the slightest provocation. On one occasion in a supermarket, Denise kicked and screamed when an elderly customer scolded her for removing cans from the shelves. Later, persistent complaints from the neighbors about uprooted flowers, dirt hurled at their doors, and overturned trash cans persuaded Denise's parents to seek help. They were told that Denise had suffered brain damage, either before or during birth. At twelve, the impairment of her ability to function took a strange form. She behaved as if there were no shutoff valves in her emotional system. This behavior did not stop at normal boundary lines. When Denise was happy, she would progress from joy to elation to silliness. Similarly, annoyance in Denise escalated until it exploded into rage. A slight disappointment would plunge her into depression. The tension of an examination at school precipitated an episode of uncontrollable trembling. Fortunately her exaggerated emotional responses yielded to medication. She obeyed strictly all instructions at school and at home. At night the effect of the drug wore off, but in a tranquil atmosphere, with little to provoke her, Denise was still able to spend a quiet evening. However, just before her parents brought her to see us, she had been suffering initardia for a period of several weeks. At night, without her medication to quiet her, exaggerated responses took over and Denise would scream and cry in frustration.

Denise's initardia was based upon a decreased capacity for sleep. She was going to bed at 9:30 and getting up at 7:00, a span of nine and one-half hours. All of the facts that we could gather led us to believe that her natural sleep span should be approximately eight and one-half hours. We recommended that a chair be brought into her room so that she could watch television while sitting in the chair, rather than in bed. We moved her bedtime forward one hour and kept her morning alarm the same, thus reducing Denise's sleep period by one full hour. Then we instructed her to eat a snack one hour before bed. Fortunately, Denise loved cheese and fruit, so that she was quite ready to obey our prescript that the snack include cheese. (Cheese is one of the foods which contains L-tryptophan, a natural substance with sleep-inducing qualities. Carbohydrates in fruit activate L-tryptophan.) Because she was a self-disciplined child, we ordered a further prescript. Denise was instructed to keep a notebook beside her bed. In the event that she could not sleep, she was to get out of bed and write in her book a list of all the programs she had seen on television that week. She never usèd the book at all. In a matter of weeks, Denise overcame her initardia.

It was crucial for Denise that she get out of bed the same time as before. It would have been a mistake to move her alarm forward, since such movement of wakening time to a later hour, for either children or adults, exposes them to the danger of a displaced sleep period within the daily cycle. Humans operate on a twenty-four-hour rhythm called a circadian rhythm. An internal clock triggers various daily changes in our biochemistry. All animals also show evidence of a clocklike mechanism, and some plants seem to operate with the aid of internal clocks. Human time mechanisms, when studied in an unchanging, isolated laboratory, maintain a twenty-five-hour cycle, rather than a twenty-four-hour cycle. Obviously, this would be most inconvenient for us. An ability by the cycle to reset itself within narrow limits permits us to modify the time to twenty-four-hours, so that our waking and sleeping conform to the rising and setting of the sun.

To give you a better idea of the relationship between the circadian cycle which we have just described and the problem of initardia, consider the case of Thelma. Thelma innocently cultivated her own case of initardia. Because she was worried and upset, she would stay awake until three or four in the morning, and then, exhausted, she slept until noon the next day. After a stretch of some months, she became accustomed, as is natural, to the situation that had disturbed her originally. But her inability to fall asleep persisted. Without realizing it, she was getting her full quota of sleep. Her sleep period was simply out of synchronization with everybody else's sleep period. On her own, Thelma tried to readjust by going to bed earlier than usual, at midnight. But when Thelma found herself unable to fall asleep at the outset of her new experiment, she immediately sabotaged her own plan by sleeping late into the next day. If this mistake seems rather obvious to you, you will be surprised to learn how many intelligent people commit the same error. The mistakes of others are clear; our own are clouded. Thelma had inadvertently converted a transient initardia into a displaced sleep period. She was able to accomplish this displacement because she had no children, whose continuous cyclic needs would have regulated her own. Also, as a writer, she could work at her own convenience, an additional factor which permitted displacement of the sleep period.

Thelma's sleep problem was fairly simple. When she delayed rising until noon, she reset her circadian cycle so that all of the biochemical events which stand in a time relationship to rising were also delayed. Therefore, her daily peak energy hour and her daily low energy point occurred later than formerly. Her receptivity to sleep was consequently also delayed—until 3:00 A.M. in her case. When Thelma began her own experiment, she should have arisen earlier and earlier each day, before she even attempted to fall asleep at night at an earlier hour. That is, she should have gradually set back her wakening alarm clock from noon to 10:00, to 9:00, and only then should she have gone to bed at midnight, instead of 3:00 A.M.. If this is your problem, remember, you cannot make a deal with the circadian cycle. You may argue with your mother; you may influence your lover; you may even persuade a Supreme Court judge; but you would be wise to obey the rules of the circadian cycle. One of the prime sleep rules is pay first, sleep later—deprivation in the morning leads to better sleep at night.

Artists, writers, and others whose work permits free-floating hours often slide into idiosyncratic cycles. Many experience no discomfort at all. We once encountered a woman who had developed the skill of restoring ancient tapestries. Museums shipped their acquisitions to her studio-apartment for repair. Quite contentedly, she worked and slept as her mood prompted, setting her alarm when necessary to wake her after a full sleep so that she could start her day, for example, at a dinner party, thus establishing her own personal sleep-wake cycle. By contrast, most people are uncomfortable in a private time world. They often complain of initardia, misperceiving the true nature of their problem. Their discomfort derives not from lack of sleep, but rather from the displacement of the sleep period within the circadian cycle. It is as if, while living in the eastern standard time zone, they set their internal clock to Pacific daylight saving time, a difference of four hours! If this is your problem, we will help you to overcome it quickly, albeit with some discomfort for a few weeks. (Incidentally, Thelma was not helped, for reasons we talk about in our final chapter.)

A weekly displacement of the sleep boundaries gives rise to the complaint—Sunday night insomnia. One would think that an adequate amount of sleep, neither too much nor too little, would not create a secondary problem. But even an adequate amount of sleep may present a puzzle, and often does—on Sunday night. Your ability to fall asleep at night is directly related to the time you awakened in the morning. The less time you have been awake, the harder it is to fall asleep. This is true of good sleepers, as well as of problem sleepers. Thus, for the average sleeper, it takes twice as long to fall asleep after ten hours of wakefulness as it does after sixteen hours of wakefulness. Someone who sleeps until noon on Sunday and then goes to bed at 10:00 on Sunday night can expect to encounter resistance to sleep. Of course, a person who usually falls asleep in two minutes would probably not notice that on Sunday night it may take four or five minutes. On the other hand, for those who normally require twenty minutes to fall asleep, twenty minutes doubled can seem like an eternity. The solution is simple; get up a little earlier, go to bed a little later. Most people are apparently willing to take the bitter with the better. They prefer to luxuriate on Sunday morning and atone on Sunday night. There is certainly nothing wrong with that decision but the point to keep in mind is that this kind of Sunday night insomnia, also available on any given Tuesday, Wednesday, or Thursday, is actually self-induced, and it is important to understand that unless practiced with restraint, innocent Sunday night insomnia could easily ripen into a full insomnia habit.

Just as the displaced sleep period is often misdiagnosed, other conditions are similarly misdiagnosed. The most dramatic instance of diagnostic error that we have seen was that of Henry.

Henry was a short man with curly brown hair. He wore gold-rimmed eyeglasses, which gave him a studious appearance. His manner was serious. He spoke slowly, considering each statement carefully. A single man in his thirties, he lived alone. In social situations, he was usually reserved. Having undergone several years of analysis, Henry was psychoanalytically oriented. He had recently terminated analysis, and while most of his difficulties were eased, one problem persisted dramatically. He could not sleep following visits with his mother! In addition, he often suffered sharp chest pains after these visits.

When the situation had first developed, he attributed an occasional sleepless night to his work. At the time, he was a copy-writer for an advertising agency. He found the position exciting and the income satisfactory. He was well accepted, with no reason to fear losing his job, and he was reasonably content most of the time. But he was envious of the rocketlike promotions of other men in the same field, some of them no older and, he thought, no cleverer than himself. With each bout of sleeplessness, he would brood about his more successful associates.

Just before the problem began, his mother, a widow, had sold her home in Poughkeepsie and moved to an apartment in the city. She was not a burden to him at all. Her time was filled by two sisters and other relatives in the city. As a matter of fact, her move made his visits to her much more convenient. He was no longer required to make the long trip to Poughkeepsie, and so now he could sleep late, after which he rather enjoyed spending a lazy afternoon and evening at her city apartment.

That year, he planned to go to Florida for the long Washington's Birthday weekend. However, it snowed too heavily for the plane to take off. Stranded at home, with no plans, no appointments, Henry spent Saturday and Sunday reading, napping, and brooding. On Sunday evening, he drifted across town to see his mother. She was serving dinner to her sister and brother-in-law. Henry joined them in a meal of sauerbraten with potato pancakes and applesauce. The conversation centered on physical ailments. After a while, dispirited, Henry departed. It was too late to see a play. No other entertainment appealed to him. Thoroughly disappointed with the entire weekend, Henry went home to bed. He was unable to fall asleep. At 11:00, he began to experience sharp chest pains. By midnight, the pains subsided, but he was now frightened. All of his fears, dissatisfactions, and tensions culminated in a storm of anxiety during the night. He decided that he needed help. A medical examination reassured him slightly. No physical basis for his pain was discovered. His heart was in good condition. A few weeks later, Henry entered psychoanalysis.

Now, with his psychoanalysis completed, Henry reviewed with us, in session after session, his remaining unresolved problem, the problem of initardia—Henry's inability to fall asleep. Our inquiries involved an effort to ascertain Henry's basic sleep-related habits, but Henry brushed many of our questions aside, preferring to concentrate on what he considered his basic problem—his reactions to his mother.

In analysis, Henry had discovered that his inability to fall asleep always occurred on the alternate Sunday after his visit to his mother. On the intervening Sundays, he played squash at an indoor court in the morning, and then usually spent the afternoon with a date or with married friends. During his analytic sessions, he had explored his relationship with his mother and had seriously considered the following possibilities as cause for his insomnia and chest pains:

His mother had infantilized him.

He had refused to give up his dependence upon his mother.

She was forcing him to play the role of her husband.

He was forcing her to play the role of his wife.

She was passively aggressive toward him.

He was passively aggressive toward her.

She was openly hostile.

He was openly hostile.

She overprotected him.

She wanted him to gratify her needs instead of his own.

He defeated his own needs in order to thwart hers.

She paid too much attention to him.

She was distant and removed from him.

He wanted her approval.

He wanted her disapproval.

Henry worked each of these formulations through, but still he could not sleep after he visited his mother. While he was pouring all of this out to us, Henry's alternate Sunday sleep problem remained fixed. Then, one day, he reported that on his sleepless Sunday night the chest pains were particularly severe. We asked him to describe the events of the entire day, starting with the moment he awakened, omitting no detail. Then, abruptly, it struck us with the force of a sonic boom!

We wrote a new prescript for Henry. He was to maintain his entire weekend routine exactly as it then existed, except for his visit to his mother, which we now insisted should *follow his squash game*! Henry agreed, and then, some three weeks later, Henry was delighted to report that he was able to fall asleep the night he visited his mother after the squash game, and the night after the next visit as well. Now it was perfectly clear. Henry had been suffering nothing more complicated than Sunday night insomnia. He had always slept late on the morning before his visit to his mother, and then, as if that were not enough, he would spend that day watching television, reading, and even drowsing a bit as well. As for the chest pains, Henry's favorite foods were corned beef and cabbage, potato pancakes with applesauce, and chocolate cheese cake. Of course, mother loved to indulge Henry with exactly those foods, and of course these foods frequently produce indigestion. In Henry's case, initardia in the form of Sunday night insomnia, because of its very simplicity, was overlooked.

If you cannot fall asleep at night, whether or not you can recognize the cause of your delayed sleep, one final word is in order. You may be worried about your inability to fall asleep. Let us remind you that the inability to fall asleep is not a pathological condition. In time of stress, in situations of hunger, when survival is at stake, a healthy animal does not sleep, but is, instead, aroused. Arousal is a life force. Envision, if you can, the millennia since the emergence of man as a separate and distinct species. Think of two million years, and five hundred thousand generations of humans, since man first stood erect. Consider the floods, the earthquakes, the migrations, the plagues, the famines, the numbing cold, the searing heat, the predators lying in wait, the pain, the grief, the persecutions, the wars through which your ancestors passed to produce you. Which quality do you think sustained them the most, the ability to sleep or the ability to stay awake, the ability to rest or the ability to seek food, to hunt for hours on end, to remain vigilant through the night, to struggle against the natural disasters they faced?

As they were energized by arousal, so we are energized by arousal. Every organism that sleeps, awakens. Every animal capable of falling asleep must also be incapable of falling asleep. When you cannot fall asleep, you are experiencing a life force. The knowledge that sleeplessness shows you to be functioning as a healthy human being will supply the tranquillity necessary for peaceful sleep.

Prescripts and Proscripts for Initardia

As you get into bed, look at your clock. Before you lie down, write the exact time on a pad at your bedside. If you have not fallen asleep after ten minutes, write the time again. If you are still awake after twenty minutes, write the time again. You must write the time after each interval. It is not enough to make a mental note of the time. If you are awake thirty minutes after your first notation, get out of bed immediately. Your very next activity is critical to your own retraining. You must, therefore, select this activity with great care. The task you choose must be sleep-inducing. In other words, it should be nonstimulating, monotonous, and it should tire your eyes. The purpose is self-evident: it should make you feel sleepy. The activity also must be entirely devoid of satisfying qualities. If you reward your wake-up mechanism with food, drink, or interesting material of any kind, you will encourage this mechanism to try the same trick again. So beware. Be a stern therapist and a good patient. Do something boring. Go back to bed only when you feel ready to sleep. If you are uncertain of what this means, consult the Back-to-Bed Guide.

You must always write the time as you get into bed. However, if after ten minutes, you are on the verge of sleep, you may postpone writing the time, but for no more than two minutes.

If after a total of twelve minutes you are still awake, you must now write the time.

If after twenty minutes you are still awake, but on the verge of sleep, you may postpone writing the time for four minutes, but no more. If after a total of twenty-four minutes you are still awake, you must now write the time no matter how sleepy you feel. After thirty minutes, you must, of course, get out of bed immediately as explained above.

You will find it difficult to collect this evidence of your wakefulness. Keep in mind that initardia is the culprit. You are the victim. As difficult as it may be to prepare your case, you cannot indict initardia without sufficient evidence. If, in a court of law, you were to present a case against the wrong defendant, no matter how convincing an argument you presented, the true culprit would still be at large to victimize you after the trial was over.

If you are awake after the specified intervals, and if you have not recorded the time *for any reason whatsoever*, stop right here. You have arrived at the moment of truth. You were asleep. Your complaint is not initardia, but hyperlixia. Give special attention to the chapter on hyperlixia.

• If you cannot fall asleep until a very late hour, and if you also sleep late into the morning, you are suffering a displaced sleep period. Your aim is to move your sleep period into a more convenient block of time. You will start the rollback by moving your alarm back, and rising one hour earlier each morning, *including weekend mornings*, for one entire week. Do not change your bedtime this first week. On the eighth day, move your alarm back one additional hour, so that you will now rise two hours earlier than originally. On the eighth night, you may go to bed one hour earlier than originally. At this point, you will be rising two hours earlier and retiring one hour earlier. It may take a few days to adjust. Do not lose heart. You may feel very tired. Don't give up. In a few days, you will have completed the transition, and you will feel comfortable. If you require a further rollback, wait for two weeks, and repeat the entire process. When you have become completely adjusted to your new sleep hours, you may wish to lengthen your sleep span. Do this gradually by adding fifteen minutes only, at either end of the period, for an entire week. On the second week, add an additional fifteen minutes to the opposite end. If, for the first week, you were to go to bed fifteen minutes earlier, then on the second week, you would set your alarm fifteen minutes later. Repeat the process until you have restored the hour you gave up.

• Remember that your ability to fall asleep quickly is directly related to the number of hours you have been awake. In order to increase prior hours of wakefulness, you may delay bedtime for forty-five minutes past your accustomed hour, or you may get out of bed forty-five minutes earlier than you usually do. You may not move both bedtime and waking time. By moving only one, either bedtime or waking time, you will not only increase prior hours of wakefulness, you will also automatically decrease total sleep time. You may wonder why you are told to *decrease* total sleep time, when your ultimate goal is to *increase* total sleep time. The reasoning is logical, although the process is circuitous. Your sleep habits are most receptive to training when you are deprived of sleep. Deprivation is a highly desirable prerequisite in any modification of habits. For example, if you as a fastidious eater wished to acquire a taste for strange new foods like pickled eels, raw fish, headcheese, or rattlesnake meat, you would do well to try them when very hungry. Similarly, in trying to develop a new sleep habit, you should be entirely ready for sleep when you get into bed. This will start the habit of falling asleep quickly. By decreasing initially your total sleep time, you will be more receptive to sleep each night, and this in itself will help you get the habit started. Only after your new habit has acquired strength may you increase your total sleep time. As a criterion, take sixteen nights of satisfactory sleep initiation. That is, when you have fallen asleep within a reasonable period for two whole weeks plus two more nights, you will then be ready to increase your total sleep time. The increase must be gradual, fifteen minutes per week until you reach your goal. If at any time you again experience a delay in the onset of sleep, you must compensate by again decreasing your total sleep time.

• Develop a presleep ritual. A ritual is a series of acts executed in a fixed order. The purpose of the presleep ritual is to give you a stronger, more immediate control over your ability to fall asleep. As an example, if you were to look at the cut surface of half a lemon, your mouth would water. Salivation, like sleep, is an automatic response. In order to induce salivation more quickly and with more certainty, you could go to your refrigerator, take out a lemon, slice it in half, and then look at it. Your mouth would have started to water before you looked at the cut half-lemon. You would be using a series of preliminary, voluntary acts to control the automatic response of salivation. Not only the sight of the lemon would then evoke salivation, but also the visual image of the lemon and each of the other separate actions that precede the sight of the lemon. The strength of each of the separate actions to control salivation is cumulative, resulting in a far greater total sum when combined than when used alone. If we were to assign arbitrary values to each step in the lemon ritual, they would read as follows:

Action	Power
Opening refrigerator	1
Picking up lemon	2
Holding lemon	3
Slicing lemon	4
Mental image of half-lemon	5
Sight of half-lemon	10
Total	25

You will note that looking at the lemon has the strongest power to elicit salivation, a power of ten. But when the other acts habitually precede the sight of the half-lemon, they form a chain. As soon as each of the preceding acts (opening the refrigerator, picking up the lemon, and the others) becomes firmly welded into the chain, it, too, gains power to elicit salivation so that, finally, even opening the refrigerator door bears a relationship to salivation. As a result, the original power of ten is converted by the ritual into a cumulative power of twenty-five. Sleep, like salivation, is an involuntary response, and like salivation it is elicited with greater strength when preceded by a habitual chain of acts—a ritual.

Athletes make excellent use of this device. Have you ever watched a diver climb the steps to the board, assume a posture, run forward, test the spring of the board, and stop? Before completion of the dive, the series is repeated several times in a predive ritual. You may argue that the posture, the run, and the little jump are part of the dive. You would be correct. But they also become ritualized to gain control of the complex coordination of the dive itself.

Baseball players also use the ritual principle in colorful, personalized styles. Do you recognize these rituals?

Robin Roberts, retired pitcher for the Philadelphia Phillies. Before every pitch, he touched his cap, touched his knee, touched his cap again, touched his knee again, and again, and again, and then finally wound up and threw the ball to the plate, usually with remarkable success.

Harry (The Hat) Walker, retired outfielder for the Pittsburgh Pirates. While at bat, in between each pitch, he would step away from the plate and fidget with his hat, taking it off and putting it back on repeatedly before stepping onto the plate to meet the next pitch. That was the reason he was nicknamed "Harry the Hat."

Hank Sauer, former outfielder for the Chicago Cubs. Between pitches, he would bounce the bat on the plate, and catch it.

Stan Musial, one of the most famous batters of all time, would swivel his hips like a chorus girl just as he crouched over the plate, after which he would proceed to hit the ball to whichever section of the ball park happened to strike his fancy.

The most colorful ritualist of all is Mark (The Bird) Fidrych.

He talks to the ground.

Then he talks to the mound.

Then he talks to the ball.

Then he turns and faces home plate.

Then he flexes his knees.

Then he juts out his rear.

Then he hunches his shoulders.

Then he lifts up his chin.

Then he stretches his neck—in a peck.

Then he bends his arms and stretches his elbows back, and high, and wide.

And then—

Only then—

He winds up for the pitch.

Fidrych, like other baseball players, uses the ritual to trigger his goal response—the precision pitch. You must develop your own ritual to trigger your goal response—sleep. You undoubtedly already employ a rudimentary ritual. Whatever else you do, or do not do, you get into your bed. Lying down in your bed is the penultimate response. Before that, you probably undress and turn out the lights. Before you read any further, make a list of those acts you already perform—for example, wash, brush teeth, open window, put on pajamas. Now add at least four more separate acts to your list. It is always preferable that your behavior grow out of your needs and your own tastes. However, the suggestions that follow may start you on the right track in devising your own ritual links.

Go to the window and scan the sky.

Brush your hair with twenty strokes.

Take out your car keys, subway token, highway toll, bus fare, or any little item you will need the next morning.

Set out a cup and saucer for your morning coffee.

Adjust the window shades.

Put your shoes in your closet.

Close all open closet doors.

Water a plant.

Rub cream on your hands.

Close your eyes and count to twenty in another language.

Or any other semiautomatic act that you can execute every night in exactly the same way.

The acts which you add to your present routine must be precise. You must be able to repeat each of them in the same way every time. When you have written your new routine, check it to make certain that it flows naturally. You must be able to repeat the series in the same order every night. It will take several weeks before the links in the ritual chain weld themselves together. When this process has been completed, sleep should automatically follow with greater speed.

In summary:
- Keep a written record of the time it takes you to fall asleep.
- Set your morning alarm back one hour earlier and get out of bed immediately when it rings. Follow this procedure for seven days.
- Do not change your bedtime.
- On the seventh evening, set your alarm back one additional hour.
- On the next evening, go to bed one hour earlier than formerly.

- You may feel fatigue during the rollback. Do not give up. Maintain your schedule.
- If necessary, repeat the rollback after an interim period of two weeks.
- After you find yourself falling asleep more promptly, you may begin to lengthen your sleep span. Add fifteen minutes in bed either in the morning or at night for one entire week. Add no more than fifteen minutes.
- Repeat the fifteen-minute addition for another entire week, and then again, until you have restored one hour.
- If at any time you again experience difficulty in falling asleep, eliminate the last additional fifteen minutes and maintain your sleep span at the previous length.
- Develop a presleep ritual.
- Practice a Somniant Technique.
- Institute an exercise program.

CHAPTER 3

Scurzomnia

Scurzomnia is short sleep. The victims of scurzomnia can fall asleep easily, but after a few hours they awaken and are unable to return to sleep again. Although they feel wide awake after only a few hours of sleep, later in the day fatigue attacks them. Their muscles ache, their eyes burn, and often an irresistible feeling of drowsiness overcomes them at inconvenient hours: while commuting, during the working day, when it is time to cook dinner, or in the early evening. In addition to severe discomfort, they are sometimes embarrassed by dozing off during social and business occasions. After a discussion of some of the causes of this particular form of insomnia, we will advise you how to overcome your own scurzomnia.

One facet of the personality of the short sleeper is described by Dr. Ernest L. Hartmann, who conducted a study comparing short sleepers to long sleepers. Though not all short sleepers are insomniacs, many insomniacs do tend to be short sleepers. Therefore, the conclusions of this study are applicable to people who suffer sleep problems. Dr. Hartmann described short sleepers as "efficient, energetic, ambitious persons who tended to work hard and to keep busy. They were relatively sure of themselves, socially adept, decisive, and were satisfied with themselves and their lives." According to Hartmann, short sleepers are in some ways less neurotic than long sleepers. They are, in a sense, "pre-programmed." By this he means that they function smoothly, using well-established, efficient habits to guide them through their work and social lives. In contrast, he found that long sleepers waste energy in needless planning. For a long sleeper, sleep is an escape. Long sleepers also spend a great deal of time in inefficient, light sleep.

Like every other sufferer, you have probably raised your eyes to heaven and asked the age-old question. "Why me?" No one knows the entire answer to that question. But some of the answer is, in fact, known. Somewhere along the way, you acquired bad sleep habits. Your personality may have made you vulnerable. Conceivably, you may have inherited a predisposition, though that is one of the unknowns.

There is, however, some evidence that speaks strongly for a prenatal determination of short sleep—that is, of a need for less sleep than the average. There are wide differences in the amount of time that infants sleep on the very first day they are born. Some infants sleep twenty-one and a half hours on the first day and thereafter, while others sleep only eleven hours on the first day and thereafter, a difference of more than ten hours per day. There is no way this difference could have been learned. It must be predetermined, either through heredity or, possibly, by prenatal conditions.

Large differences persist all through life, although less dramatically, as total sleep time diminishes for all. Professor Morgan, who taught at Stanford University, was known to sleep only four hours per night. He had slept for eight hours each night until he was in his early twenties when suddenly, and without precipitating causes that he could recall, he found himself awakening consistently after only four hours of sleep. This decreased need persisted for the rest of his life, almost sixty additional years. His claim was verified in the sleep laboratory at Stanford. He was not, however, an insomniac. He awakened after his four hours feeling vigorous and refreshed. An even shorter verified record is held by two Australian men, who each required less than three hours of sleep a night, and who functioned comfortably and efficiently with only that minimal amount of sleep.

Short sleep by itself is not an insomnia problem; scurzomnia is determined by the stressful aspects of your short sleep. These are the aspects with which we must deal in order to make you more comfortable and to enable you to sleep for longer periods.

Severe depression can lead to scurzomnia. One hot August evening, we received a telephone call from a woman who sounded desperate. She wanted to see us about her daughter, Mala, a college student. Mother and daughter appeared at our office early the next morning. Born and raised in the United States, Mala was Chinese. She was a girl who would look pretty and pert if she smiled, but she did not smile at all. She was gloomy. Her denim shorts and trainman's scarf suggested indifference rather than youthful spontaneity. Mala's mother did most of the talking. It was clear that Mala's intense depression, compounded by insomnia, had induced her mother to investigate sleep therapy. An honor student in music at Oberlin College, Mala was entering her junior year, but had been suffering scurzomnia for weeks, and was concerned that she would be unable to return to school on Labor Day if she could not start to sleep more fully before then. Neither the mother nor the daughter was responsive when we asked gently about the precipitating cause of the depression. As a matter of fact, the mother reminded us that she had heard us explain at a lecture that life always presented problems, and that while we could not cure life's problems, we could nevertheless help people to sleep in spite of their problems. We sensed that Mala and her mother would have talked more freely had either of them visited us separately, and subsequently this impression proved accurate.

It was clear that the only possibility of helping Mala in time for the opening of school lay in a crash course, and that we would have to see her every day for the following two weeks. Before the program was designed, we explained that in cases of severe depression insomnia was only one of many effects, and the depression itself required treatment on a long-term basis. Mala volunteered that she was already in the care of a psychiatrist, and that her psychiatrist had agreed that sleep counseling, at this point, might be helpful.

Mala kept every appointment promptly. She arrived alone and she was never late. During the sessions, she seldom spoke. Unless our questions were directly related to sleep, she found them alarming. She would pause for a long time and then demand to know whether we asked everyone the same questions, or why we required the requested information. She was obviously worried that we would consider her mentally disturbed. At the same time, logical explanations reassured her at once. We learned that she was studying musical composition and had composed three short works that were scheduled to be presented at the next school concert. We also surmised that her social skill was poor, and that both at school and at home she was essentially companionless. She seemed preoccupied almost exclusively with her studies, and it required no deep analysis to appreciate that Mala was not really enjoying her life at all.

The information that Mala offered was supplied in a faintly metallic, expressionless voice. She did not elaborate. When we spoke, she kept her eyes lowered most of the time, although she did look up occasionally. Her eyes were brown and filled with an oceanic grief. In a few phrases, she explained that early in the spring she had started to see a young man whom she had known casually in high school. They had enjoyed a few afternoons and evenings together. As far as we could determine, no deep emotional experience had been shared by the two. Perhaps he was only expressing friendship when he told Mala that he was homosexual. As for Mala, her reaction was apathetic at first, but over the course of the next few days, an overwhelming sense of loss engulfed her. She lost interest in everything and she did not sleep.

Several factors contributed to a poor prognosis for Mala. It was immediately clear that her depression had not been caused by her friend's homosexuality, but had been lying dormant only to be triggered by this disappointment. Furthermore, her condition was unlikely to change within a few weeks, either spontaneously or as a result of psychotherapy. She was uncommunicative, so we had little knowledge of her habits. Most important, neither Mala nor we knew how much she slept. She went to bed at eleven every night and lay awake for several hours. At about two in the morning, it was her custom to get up to take a sleeping pill. She estimated that she fell asleep at about three and awakened at seven. She was then so tired that she could not get out of bed, and so she lay there drowsing on and off until noon. Mala estimated that she slept only four hours a night. Yet she was *in bed* for thirteen hours. There simply was no way of knowing how much she actually slept while honestly believing herself to be awake.

To balance out the negative factors, there were others in her favor. She was instinctively motivated, as are all people, toward health. She revealed her motivation in her promptness for appointments, and in her vigilant attention to all of our instructions and explanations. Then, too, she appreciated that we liked her, and she liked us in return; we had a good relationship. She was able to accept our help. Finally, her intelligence and the resiliency of youth were perhaps the most helpful elements of all.

Mala followed all instructions faithfully. In a few days, she admitted grudgingly that she was sleeping somewhat better, a little more deeply, a little longer. She experienced one or two setbacks in the days that followed. As with all of our participants, it was not necessary that she tell us when she had experienced a bad night. The bad night was mirrored on her face when she arrived in the morning. On the whole, improvement was steady, but slow. Two days before Labor Day, Mala requested permission to delay her return to school. Then, two weeks after the fall semester had started, with many misgivings and with reluctance, she said goodbye and left for college. We spoke to her on the telephone to remind her to follow instructions and to encourage her to persist. A few letters were exchanged. She visited us at Thanksgiving, and then again at Christmas. These sessions were devoted to extending moral support so that she would not fall back into her habit of spending most of her time in bed. When Mala finally left us, her sleep habits had improved, and she was experiencing reasonable comfort at night. We are not suggesting that we cured Mala's depression. That was a long-term problem. But Mala's sleep pattern was something else. There, we helped her materially, so that despite her depression she could at least fall asleep, remain asleep, and waken without exhaustion. The directives we supplied to Mala are the same directives we will supply to you at the end of this chapter.

Scurzomnia cases are often difficult to diagnose and treat because of variations in the amount of sleep required by different individuals. Unlike other types of insomnia, which can be evaluated on an objective basis, the diagnosis of scurzomnia rests on a secondary effect, the individual's perception of sleep as inadequate. Some people feel that their sleep is inadequate when they notice that they are sleeping less than formerly, but this is natural. The number of hours you sleep, and even the number of hours your friend, the good sleeper, sleeps, has probably been decreasing as each of you grows older.

Sleep time (with a few exceptions) naturally decreases from infancy to childhood, from childhood to young adulthood, and then continues to decrease until old age, at which point it may reverse its course and start increasing. One study of college students found that the average sleep length was eight hours and five minutes for both males and females. Other studies reveal that sleep length dropped to less than seven hours on the average as people reached their late twenties, and fell to six hours by age sixty. Remember that these are averages. An average falls somewhere near the middle of the range. Half the people who constitute the average sleep more than the average figure, but at the same time the other half mentioned sleep less than these figures. This means that at college age half the population sleeps less than eight hours per night. After college age, half the population sleeps less than seven hours per night. What does this say about the eight-hour myth? That it is exactly that, a myth. Nothing more nor less than a myth.

The belief that eight hours is necessary has caused more anxiety and, as a result, more sleep problems than any other factor we can think of. A dire, unnamed fate is supposed to lie in wait for those who sleep less than eight hours. No one has ever discovered that fate. *All investigations show that the short sleeper is just as healthy, just as vigorous, as the long sleeper.* Read that sentence again and repeat it to yourself. Neither heart attacks, nor strokes, nor cancer, nor any other serious ailments have been associated with lack of sleep. Many people firmly believe that lack of sleep leads to a lined and haggard face and to black rings under the eyes. If that is so, one should be able to pick out poor sleepers just by looking at them. We cannot. Can you? We once led a group which included two beautiful young women, both with clear, glowing skins. At the first meeting, a middle-aged bachelor, also a member of the group, stared in disbelief. "Is this what insomnia makes you look like?" he asked. "Maybe it's not such a bad idea."

This does not mean that you do not have insomnia if you feel that you do not sleep sufficiently. If you are uncomfortable, if you are exhausted, you do have a sleep problem. Nobody knows better than you how you feel. The greatest physician in the world does not know as much about your comfort or discomfort as you do. We emphasize, however, that loss of sleep, in and of itself, will not produce any physical deterioration, and is therefore no reason for anxiety on that score.

The alleviation of anxiety cleared up one of our cases of scurzomnia almost miraculously. Lila was a wholesome-looking woman in her forties. She was an individual who accommodated interesting contradictions in her personal style. She was a kindergarten teacher, but quite sophisticated. She was a health food enthusiast who enjoyed martinis. She was an athlete who dressed like a model. Additionally, and here she was consistent all the way, she took excellent care of her face and her body. She danced at the Alvin Ailey Studio at least once a week, and she rode a bicycle from Chinatown to the Upper East Side for additional exercise. When she came to us, she had been awakening at 5:00 A.M., unable to fall asleep again. She would lie in bed until after seven, her usual waking time. She said that the worst part of her problem was that she knew she would look tired and drawn the next day, with dark circles under her eyes, which only increased her anxiety.

We explained carefully to Lila the physiology of lack of sleep—that whatever else it may do, it does not, by itself, bring lines to the face or circles under the eyes. This was crucial—we assured her that every responsible study of insomnia supported that basic proposition. When Lila could accept that as an established first premise, she was ready for an alteration in her sleep behavior. One directive was critical to a change in her sleep pattern. She was told to get out of bed when she awakened at five, and to start her day immediately. Moreover, she was advised *not to go to bed before her regular bedtime the following night,* and to set her alarm, in case she needed it, for six-thirty, instead of seven. She experienced a number of bad days, but in a short time her sleep pattern adjusted itself. Her awakening time became regular. She slept almost an hour less than she had been sleeping, because she was undergoing the natural decrease we just discussed. But most important, she was no longer anxious about diminished sleep. She looked rested. Lila finally understood that the lines in her face when she had slept less than the eight-hour-myth level resulted from her apprehensions and her low spirits rather than from the loss of sleep itself.

Our treatments for scurzomnia are directed at four objectives:

1. The consolidation of sleep into one solid block of time. When this is accomplished, sleep stages proceed in their normal sequence and provide a greater sense of well-being.

2. The relocation of the sleep period into a more convenient time slot, so that sleep hours and waking hours coincide, as far as possible, with those of most other people.

3. The alleviation of conscious or unconscious worry, which operates as an energy drain and which, in and of itself, prevents sleep.

4. The extension of the sleep period so that it lasts significantly longer.

You can improve the quantity, as well as the quality, of your sleep. However, like everyone else, your capacity for sleep is limited by a ceiling that is built into your own biological clock. If you are sleeping for three hours each night, you probably will not be able to increase your sleep period to seven hours, although you may increase it to five hours. At that point, you may actually feel an increase in physical comfort, but nevertheless remain dissatisfied, because you still have extra waking hours with nothing to fill them. To those of you who do not know how to deal with those empty waking hours, we offer one suggestion to consider.

If you were offered a gift of three extra years of life, would you refuse that gift? Would you accept the three extra years, even if some unusual conditions were attached? Here are the conditions. The three years are to be divided into short periods which will be inserted regularly into your normal life span. During these regular periods, conversation with others will be sharply limited. You will be within easy reach of everyone you know, but you will spend the time alone. It will be dark outside, but you will have lights available. Given those conditions, would you then refuse these extra years of life? Would you consider yourself fortunate or unfortunate? Would other people pity you or envy you? How in fact would you spend those three years? How would you fill them?

If you sleep five hours per night instead of the mythical eight, then, putting everything else aside, you have actually received forty-five days of extra life each year. In twenty years you will have accrued three extra years in which to live. Is this a cause for anxiety, sufficient to refuse those extra years? Are the conditions so noxious that you cannot enjoy the extra time? Surely not. Surely you will want to take the extra hours and fill them with pleasure.

We are not suggesting that you cannot or will not sleep longer and more restfully. If you follow, conscientiously, our prescripts and proscripts, you will without question achieve agreeable, gratifying sleep. We suggest that sleep is often a will-o'-the-wisp, more easily captured with a less intense pursuit.

Prescripts and Proscripts for Scurzomnia

· Exercise is extremely effective in increasing sleep time. (As a point of interest, pregnancy, starvation, and circumcision also increase sleep time, but you may not find these feasible.) The exercise must be vigorous and continuous. Housework does not qualify, nor does strolling or window-shopping. The exercise should be undertaken before 4 P.M. if at all possible. With the consent of your physician, plan an exercise regimen. Start with thirty minutes each day, and gradually increase the time to an hour. The type of exercise you choose does not matter, but it should produce muscular fatigue. Brisk, sustained walking, bicycling, and jogging are excellent. Jogging time will, of course, involve less than one hour, and will depend on your own particular tolerance. Competitive sports help some people but serve to stimulate others too much, and so we do not recommend competitive activities. Your aim is tired relaxation.

· Go to bed one hour later than is your custom. You may have difficulty postponing your bedtime. Some scurzomniacs find it difficult to stay awake early in the evening. The way to attack this problem is to plan a number of projects to interest you in the evening, after dinner and before bedtime. The projects must definitely exclude passive activities like reading or television. You will be able to remain awake only if you are involved in an activity that stimulates your small muscles as well as your mind. You are the only one who can decide which activities are best for you. Suggested types of activities are painting, drawing, woodworking, sewing, cooking, baking, construction work of all kinds, electrical work, and other active hobbies.

• Stop your activity about a half hour before your new bedtime. If you feel wide awake at this time, practice a presleep ritual, described at the end of Chapter Two. A simple ritual should be followed, even after your sleep problems have disappeared. It will help you to maintain rapid sleep initiation.

• When you awaken in the morning, look at the clock. If it is too early for you to want to get up, wait for five minutes, and if you are still awake, use a Somniant Technique. *Windows on the World* and *The Sleep Swing* are particularly effective at this time. Remain in bed for only a total of thirty minutes. If you have not fallen back to sleep by then, get out of bed and start your day. But do not start it by eating breakfast or by drinking coffee. It's all right to have water and four ounces of juice. Nothing else until later. You do not wish to reward early awakening or to get yourself into the habit of waking up to have an early breakfast. Delay breakfast until the time you consider reasonable. Eat at the same time you would have eaten had you experienced a full night's sleep.

• Do not worry about the sleep you have lost. No one ever died from lack of sleep. Much of your discomfort after a bad night results from anxiety rather than from the sleep loss. Your present anxiety about sleep will not change easily. It is one thing to tell yourself not to worry; it is quite another to obey your own instructions. You must change your deep-seated attitude toward sleep. You can use a method that has proven extremely effective in producing attitude change. In order to do this, make your own mental list of evidence that shows loss of sleep to be harmless. You can also consult our partial listing on page 9. Familiarize yourself thoroughly with the items on your list. Then speak to an interested person—your spouse, a friend, someone else who complains of insomnia, if possible. Explain that short sleep is harmless, and convince that other person. Your assignment is to make certain that your listener is impressed by your facts. That is your entire technique. This method has been widely used to produce attitude change in a variety of social and interpersonal relations. We have used it successfully to alleviate anxiety, even in individuals who could not recognize that they were suffering anxiety about their scurzomnia.

• Do not take a nap no matter how tired you feel. Do not lie down, even for a few minutes. Your capacity for sleep is limited. Whatever sleep you take during the day is subtracted from the sleep of the following night. It is not added to the sleep of the past night. Think of sleep as money in the bank. You cannot withdraw your money now and again later. Save it for when you need it most, at night.

• Do not lie down in the middle of the day, no matter how tired you feel. Lying down counts as sleep time, and you must consider it as sleep, even though you may be wide awake. Do not allow yourself to doze. If you find yourself dozing on a train, a common experience, you should stand up. We know this will be extremely difficult. We understand just how painful it can be to discipline yourself in this way, but if you allow yourself to doze, you will be squandering good sleep time that you cannot afford to waste. Your daytime sleepiness will disappear just as soon as your sleep pattern is adjusted. The inconvenience is temporary. The improvement is permanent.

In summary:
• Exercise vigorously every day, preferably before 4:00 P.M.
• Delay your bedtime for one hour.
• Practice a Somniant Technique upon awakening during the night.
• Do not remain in bed awake for more than thirty minutes.
• When you get out of bed in the early morning, start your day immediately. However, remember to delay breakfast to a normal breakfast hour.
• Do not nap.

CHAPTER 4

Hyperlixia

Hyperlixia is our term for an excessive amount of light sleep. It is a common form of insomnia, but one that frequently goes unrecognized—and untreated—by its victims, because many believe they spend the night awake, though in fact they are sleeping lightly.

Light sleep is not, in and of itself, an ailment. It is normal to spend as much as ten or twelve percent of sleep time in light sleep. The trouble is introduced when the time is extended beyond reasonable limits, when it steals from deeper, more comfortable sleep. Yes, hyperlixia steals time. It is a thief. It also disguises itself as wakefulness. It is an imposter as well as a thief.

Until the early 1950s knowledge of sleep was restricted to a few basic propositions: that we sleep lightly and deeply, that we may sleep both lightly and deeply on the same night, and finally, that we dream. In the fifties, the *electroencephalogram* (EEG) was first used to reveal what had previously been concealed beneath closed eyelids. Although on a superficial level the EEG merely confirmed the facts with which we were already familiar, its deeper revelations were startling. Even today, more than twenty years later, you may be surprised to learn that every night you pass through five different types of sleep. At times, during the night, you are paralyzed; you cannot move. Your heart pounds; your blood pressure shoots up. You breathe like a long-distance runner. Your eyes race back and forth under closed lids. You experience several sexual arousals. You awaken momentarily, but you do not remember the awakenings. You turn at predictable moments. You may, if you wish, set an automatic physical alarm system, which will awaken you at any signal you specify. Incidentally, you also rest.

Think of sleep as a series of levels, five altogether, one of which houses a cinema which we patronize regularly. We descend, then ascend, then descend through these levels all through the night. Before we fall asleep, we start at Stage 0, which is the entry point. Stage 0 is a presleep condition in which we are completely relaxed. We are still awake, but our eyes are closed, and as we engage in lazy daydreams, or half-formulated thoughts, our eyes may drift slowly from one side to the other. The movements are brief, and sleep scientists speculate that they probably coincide with an imagined visual image. During this presleep period, our brains transmit what is known as an alpha wave, an electrical impulse which is recorded by the EEG apparatus as a series of waves on a moving sheet of paper. The alpha wave appears in Stage 0 when, although we are still awake, we are completely relaxed in preparation for sleep. Then, from this Stage 0 presleep period we progress to Stage 1, actual sleep, and this is signaled by a slow rolling motion of the eyes. If you wish, you may alert yourself, before you retire, to note the slow rolling sensation just as you are shifting from Stage 0 presleep to Stage 1 sleep. In a few nights, you will probably grow aware of the eye movement as it occurs.

Following the alpha wave, the onset of sleep is precipitous. One second we are awake, and one instant later we are fast asleep. We have now descended to Stage 1. Most people are astonished to learn that sleep arrives abruptly—our sensations encourage the belief that we drift into sleep by languorous degrees. The suddenness of sleep onset was dramatically illustrated in one particular study of vision. An experimental subject agreed to go to sleep with his eyes taped open. As he was falling asleep, a bright light was flashed every two seconds. The subject was instructed to move his finger each time the light was flashed. He obeyed the instruction for several minutes, but then suddenly he missed a flash. He was immediately asked why he had not moved his finger. The subject was amazed. Even with his eyes taped open, he had fallen asleep instantly somewhere in the two-second interval, and he had failed to see the flashing light. Interestingly enough, there are many who habitually sleep with their eyes open. In all cases, despite the open eyes, the sleeper is functionally blind, and sees nothing during sleep.

One of our participants mastered the trick of sleeping with her eyes open, and she described the experience to us. Sandy was a young woman who suffered insomnia immediately following a divorce. Her insomnia was transitory, an emotional reaction to the divorce. When Sandy and Jerry first met, they were attracted to each other instantly. Jerry was a sports addict. Sandy's interest in sports was lukewarm at best. But although Sandy did not like sports, she did like Jerry. And so, during the summer of their courtship, they went to baseball games. In the fall, they went to football games. In the winter, they went to basketball games. In between, they went to hockey games, track meets, prizefights, and even to an occasional wrestling match. It never occurred to Jerry that Sandy did not enjoy sporting events. It never occurred to Sandy that Jerry's fanaticism would continue into marriage. But it did continue into marriage, and at most of the games Sandy was utterly bored and could barely stay awake. Still in love, and reluctant to offend Jerry, she kept her eyes wide open, even as she fell asleep.

One night during a group meeting, Sandy recounted the experience of sleeping with her eyes open. She described a baseball game on a summer night. Under the artificial lights, the field was a vivid green. The uniforms of the players gleamed a fluorescent white. Here and there, a touch of red on a sleeve, a stripe of blue on a cap, struck her eye. After the early innings of the game, when Sandy had exhausted all of the faint interest she could muster, she amused herself with daydreams. Occasionally, she reached out to touch Jerry's hand, finding reassurance in the answering squeeze of his fingers. Soon, with eyes fixed open, she fell asleep, and as she did, the players, the umpires, the uniforms, the green grass itself disappeared. Only streaks of color remained. Sandy saw flashes of green, broken by blotches of white and stripes of blue, and that was all. According to Sandy, she was able to see color for some time after form had disappeared. Finally, she saw nothing at all. Her description reveals that, although sleep onset is sudden, loss of vision during sleep is somewhat more gradual when eyes remain open, with form fading first, and color ebbing later. As for the marriage, when Sandy finally resisted attending the games, Jerry decided that Sandy had deceived him by accompanying him so religiously during their courtship. Sandy could not understand how a demonstration of love could have been a deception. In any event, although the chemical attraction persisted for both of them, their particular chemicals did not possess enough bonding power to hold their marriage together.

It is during the first actual sleep stage, Stage 1, that we experience the myoclonic spasm known as the sleep start. You have seen infants react to a loud noise with a startle response. They exhibit the same response during sleep. You yourself may remember experiencing the sensation of falling while asleep. This is the typical sleep start. Additionally, there are myoclonias which are confined to a portion of the body. One of our participants, Al, a dynamic and productive man who was involved in many activities calculated to produce tension, discovered his spasms obliquely. He began to notice, with increasing frequency, tiny blisters on his tongue, and while his physician attached no importance to them, nevertheless both Al and the doctor were mystified. Then, one night, Al solved the mystery. Just as he fell abruptly into Stage 1 sleep, his jaw, completely relaxed only one moment earlier, snapped shut in a quick spasm. Two of his back teeth caught the edge of his tongue between their sharp points, and because the contact was particularly cutting, it wakened him immediately, producing a blister which remained painful for several days. Al was offered two options. He could take, on a continuing basis, a drug to relax his muscles, or he could suffer the blisters. He selected the blisters.

Stage 1 is also the host of the hypnagogic image. As we fall asleep, we may occasionally see a clear image. It can seem quite real, so much so that we are not able to distinguish the image from an actual event. Members of our groups have also reported auditory experiences as they fell asleep. They hear a word, or a phrase, or even a full sentence. The visual and the auditory experiences originate from within; they are not part of the external world, but they do seem real, especially when they immediately precede awakening. If the images contain unrealistic elements, as dreams often do, we dismiss them. If they are realistic but innocuous, we generally forget them without further considera- tion. When, however, the images are both lifelike and meaningful, serious misconceptions may follow. A husband may argue with his wife, a child feel hurt by a parent, all because of hypnagogic images they feel were part of their actual life experience.

A devastating encounter was suffered by one of our mem- bers. Because of the special clarity of one of her hypnagogic images experienced at home while partially incapacitated with a sprained ankle, she became certain that she had hallucinated and that she was therefore on the brink of a serious nervous disorder. Resting in bed to counter the fatigue of hobbling around the house, she was absolutely positive that she saw her husband float in mid-air from the living room to the bedroom, and then settle slowly, like a helicopter, into his own bed. Our careful explana- tion of the hypnagogic image, that it was a common by-product of sleep and was not at all connected with mental disorder, relieved her apprehensions. You may wonder why the experience is called a hypnagogic image rather than a dream. It does seem to be a dream, or rather a fragment of a dream, but it differs from a dream in one respect. The dream consists of a series of events which follow each other like scenes in a motion picture. The hypnagogic image is usually a single event. It lacks the scenario factor—the element of plot development which plays an important part in every dream.

Experimental subjects who are awakened from Stage 1 sleep are the source of yet another phenomenon which occurs in this stage. They report that while asleep they were actually thinking. They describe the thought processes which occur during sleep. The thoughts may be as rational as "I left my umbrella at the office," or "I'll take care of those letters first thing in the morn- ing." On the other hand, it is equally possible that the thoughts may be quite irrational: "People are plotting against me," or "I'm awake. Why can't I fall asleep?"

It is this last pernicious thought which creates so much difficulty for insomniacs. Not only does this specific thought occur to many people while they are actually asleep, it seems to recur over and over and over again to the very same people, who then insist that they have been awake when they were, in fact, sleeping.

Let us assure you here and now that this is not a psychotic process; it is not a manifestation of mental illness. It is simply a mistaken perception.

An artist acquaintance of ours described how he experienced this very confusion, and how he discovered, with the aid of purely coincidental factors, that his presumed wakefulness was actually sleep. One wintry night, long before morning, he awakened. Because he customarily slept through the night, he was surprised, but he was not uncomfortable. When he turned his head toward the window he could see a pale moon. Turning back, he saw a painting on the opposite wall illuminated by a rectangular shaft of moonlight. He was looking at his own canvas, one of his favorites, with an indistinct house in its background. In the foreground, streaks of gray, orange, and yellow suggested two human figures among shadowed trees. He stared at the canvas with fond admiration, wondering at the same time why he did not fall asleep. And now, something most peculiar happened. As he looked at his painting, the two figures were projected in three dimensions, as if they had been executed in bas-relief. But he had painted them flat—he was absolutely certain he had painted them flat. Puzzled, he turned away and faced the window. Still, the puzzle annoyed him, and so he turned back to look at the painting once more. Yes, it was a bas-relief. Definitely!

Definitely? Bas-relief? He raised himself on one elbow to get a closer look, and he squeezed his eyes shut, counted to five, opened his eyes, and stared at the painting once again. It was not a bas-relief at all. It was the same vivid two-dimensional oil that he remembered painting. Slowly, and a bit confused, he lowered himself back onto the bed.

In the morning, he remembered the incident, and he struggled to resolve the enigma. There were, he appreciated finally, only two alternative explanations. Either the canvas had actually changed twice during the night or the bas-relief interval was only a dream. Not simply a dream about the painting, but also a dream that he was awake, followed by an actual awakening, when the bas-relief finally returned to its original two dimensions. Although the first alternative, that the painting had been transfigured, was more intriguing, he was reluctantly forced to choose the second one. He had experienced the fragment of a dream embodying both the thought (I am awake) and the image (the painting is three-dimensional).

Actually, it is not necessary to experience directly the thought "I am awake." The subjective impression of wakefulness during Stage 1 sleep is rather common. In one particular experiment, the subjects were awakened out of actual sleep. With each of the subjects, brain waves showed typical Stage 1 patterns. Additionally, closed eyes, regular breathing, and total observable behavior also revealed sleep. Yet sixty percent of the sleeping subjects claimed that they had been awake! The results of this experiment offer convincing evidence of how frequently we mistake light sleep for wakefulness. The error presents no problem where insomnia is not a problem. However, in cases where the Stage 1 light sleep is extended beyond ten minutes, the feeling of wakefulness becomes extremely uncomfortable, and must be dispelled before the victim can find relief. If this is your difficulty, we will help you to conquer the obsessive impression that you are awake when in fact you are sleeping. We will also teach you how to speed your descent from Stage 1 to a deeper, more restful sleep.

Stage 1 sleep usually continues for approximately ten minutes, after which the wavy lines of the EEG describe a new pattern, the K complex of Stage 2. In Stage 2 sleep, a deeper sleep than Stage 1, the relaxation process, which actually began during Stage 0 presleep, and which continued during Stage 1 sleep, now makes further progress. Breathing is regular, deeper, and slow. Heart rate decreases. Body temperature declines. The voluntary muscles, those muscles which we move at will, relax to a greater extent. The sleeper is at rest. But this is only temporary, as we shall see when we delve into the nature of dreams. If, during Stage 2 sleep, your husband or your wife were to enter your bedroom, you would not awaken. If, on the other hand, a houseguest or a stranger were to enter, you would wake up immediately, and you would probably realize that you had been asleep. Eighty-five percent of experimental subjects who were awakened from Stage 2 sleep acknowledged that they had been asleep. However, ten percent claimed that they had been awake, and five percent did not know whether they had been awake or asleep. We can see, therefore, that even in the relatively deep Stage 2 sleep, a good number of insomniacs suffer the mistaken impression that they are actually awake.

As we drift from Stage 2 down to Stage 3 sleep, the EEG pen describes deeper and wider-rolling curves known as delta waves. It will require a louder noise to arouse you now. Your muscles relax even further. You breathe evenly. Your heart rate slows, your temperature continues its decline, and your blood pressure continues its fall. Comparatively little is known about Stage 3 sleep; it is generally dismissed as a transition phase. We can expect that breakthroughs in the knowledge of sleep will illuminate as yet unsuspected Stage 3 events.

Stage 3 occupies a relative small portion of the night. From Stage 3, we sink into Stage 4, the deepest sleep of all. The high, rolling EEG delta waves which appeared during Stage 3 now dominate the record of neural activity. If you could observe yourself during this Stage 4 period, you would see little or no motion. A noise would still register on your brain, but it would not rouse you until it became persistent. Then you would surface into consciousness slowly, emerging from sleep with a sense of confusion. You may recall having been awakened by the telephone at some time. Do you remember a brief struggle to decide exactly what had awakened you, and to determine where you were? When arousal is accompanied by this kind of confusion, it is probably arousal from Stage 4 sleep. If, for some reason, you were to be deprived of Stage 4 sleep for one night or for several consecutive nights, you would build up a Stage 4 deficit. You would then compensate for the Stage 4 deficit on the following nights by remaining in Stage 4 sleep for a longer period than is your habit. The same deficit compensation occurs after a loss of dream sleep, but Stage 1 and Stage 2 are not similarly affected. Paradoxically, as we shall see, this stage may become the backdrop for strange and frightening events. It is during Stage 4 that episodes of pavor nocturnus (night terrors), enuresis (bed-wetting), and somnambulism (sleepwalking) occur. One might say that, while Stage 2 ushers us into a theatre of comedy and drama, Stage 4 is a theatre of mystery.

It takes approximately sixty minutes to descend from entry into Stage 1 to Stage 4. The cycle does not end here. At the close of the Stage 4 period, we start an ascent back up into Stage 3, to Stage 2, and finally to Stage 1. Although individual variations are seen, movement from stage to stage continues in roughly regular progression until waking. Four to five complete cycles are traversed during each night.

About ninety minutes after we have fallen asleep, and passed down through Stages 1 through 4, and then up through Stage 3 and Stage 2, we stand in the cinema between Stage 2 and Stage 1 where now the first drama of the night begins. The film is about to start. In a moment or two, a dream will start to unfold. First, there is a shift in the position of the body. Many people have told us that they sleep quietly, with little or no movement during the night. This impression is incorrect. In males, penile erection occurs, lasting through the dream period. The erection occurs in little boys as well as grown men. Females also show peripheral sexual arousal which is less easily noticed. In addition, voluntary muscles become paralyzed. Beneath the eyelids, but clear even to casual observation, the eyes can be seen to race back and forth. The dream has begun.

Contrary to popular belief, the dream takes as much time when it is projected upon the mind's eye as it would take projected upon a motion picture screen. A number of studies have shown that the eyes of the dreamer continue to move just as if the dream were unfolding on a motion picture screen. In a dream of a tennis match, the dreamer's eyes move from side to side. In a dream of a mountain climber, the eye movement is vertical. Readings taken from the auditory nerve, which carries sound impulses to the brain, show that the dreamer seems to be hearing the sounds in the dream just as if those sounds were actually there.

As the drama of the dream unfolds, so does the drama of the autonomic nervous system. It is during the dream that the heart pounds out its hammering rhythm, that the blood pressure shoots up, only to subside, then perhaps to shoot up again. Breathing becomes rapid and irregular. Sometimes, breathing ceases momentarily, as if the dreamer were holding his breath. Adrenalin reaches its highest daily concentration in the body. Brain temperature, which has been declining, rises. The wild storm of activity contrasts sharply with the slackened muscles which paralyze the dreamer. The muscles of the neck turn off, as if a switch has been pulled. For the duration of the dream, the muscles lack the power to support the head and chin.

The amount of activation varies from dream to dream. Strangely enough, the highest levels of excitation may often accompany the mildest of dreams. One dreamer, awakened from a hurricane of neural activity, reported that he had been dreaming that he was eating an ice-cream cone in a park. Obviously, intense levels of excitation sometimes do accompany dreams of violence. You can surely recall awakening from a nightmare with your heart hammering. If you remember the details of the nightmare, this indicates you have probably wakened during the dream itself, or shortly after its conclusion. Most of the time, however, we are completely unaware of our other life, acted out under the cover of closed eyes and limp muscles.

Just as abruptly as the dream began, the dream ends. All of the intensified body activity subsides. Snoring resumes. Voluntary muscles regain their power to shift the position of the body once more. The rapid eye movements (REMs) cease.

After the dream, the sleeper returns to the light sleep of Stage 1 before the slow descent through the stages is initiated once more. The first dream period is the shortest dream period of the night. Succeeding dreams last longer, each dream occupying a greater period of time than its predecessor.

In contrast to the dreams, which lengthen with each succeeding cycle, the deep sleep of Stage 4 decreases in length as the night ticks away. Stage 4 sleep appears only in the first two or three cycles of each night, and in older people it may occur only once, or possibly not at all. While young adults spend an average of fifteen percent of the night in Stage 4 deep sleep, this stage shrinks to an average of only five percent for older people, and, moreover, the portion of their deep sleep which has been taken away is replaced by Stage 1 light sleep. To put it another way, while young persons spend only five percent of their sleep time in Stage 1 light sleep, the period expands to ten or twelve percent in later maturity. Accepting these percentages, the adult over forty who sleeps for a six-hour span may expect, in this period, slightly more than half an hour of Stage 1 light sleep. When we examine sleep patterns carefully, we see that the average time spent in Stage 0 (falling asleep) adds another half-hour to the perception of wakefulness. Now we have one half-hour of a presleep period when the person is actually awake, plus one half-hour of Stage 1 light sleep, often perceived as actual wakefulness, for a total of one full hour of possible distress time. If this is your problem, our task is dual. First we must shorten Stage 0 presleep to a more acceptable level. Then we must rob Stage 1 light sleep of the illusion that it is wakefulness rather than actual and restful sleep.

Another source of distress springs from a variation of the typical sleep pattern. You have seen that sleep usually travels from one stage to an adjacent stage. EEG studies have also shown that some light sleepers oscillate between a waking state, Stage 0, and Stage 1, or even Stage 2 sleep. They tend to remember the waking period, while forgetting entirely the major portion of the night which is spent in sleep. In one of our cases, the misapprehension of the sleeper was discovered during a shocking midnight scene of terror. Isme, a Moroccan woman in her fifties, was escorted to all group meetings by her husband, Davi, who waited patiently outside to drive her home. They had been married for more than thirty years, and were United States residents for almost all of that period. He was thin, with a stooped posture, but a vivacious manner. His command of the language was better than that of Isme, who, in spite of her years in New York City, spoke heavily accented, barely intelligible English. Isme made housekeeping her career. Her social contacts were restricted to other Middle Eastern women. Davi, on the other hand, was more cosmopolitan, and had mastered English completely, while building a prosperous fresh produce trade in the wholesale food markets near the New York City docks.

Isme was a slender, pleasant woman who displayed the emotional maturity of a pampered ten-year-old child. Because her background was exotic, her clothes exquisite, and her manner engaging, the other members of the group did not resent her egocentric behavior, at least not openly. For several weeks, Isme persisted in giving a full description of her inability to sleep *at all.* When we advised her to get out of bed while awake, she stared blankly, snapping off her attention abruptly, as if it were a light switch. When members of the group offered sympathetic suggestions she would respond with an excellent, if difficult-to-follow, explanation as to why she could not possibly pursue that particular course of action. She dismissed the possibility of hyperlixia as utter nonsense. She was awake. All night. Furthermore, she claimed that she could give a detailed account of every sound, every outside movement, every passing automobile during the entire long sleepless night, and, as a matter of fact, she often rendered just such an account to Davi in the morning.

As for Davi, he attested to the truth of Isme's claim. Before she registered for our group, he described, in detail, her inability to sleep, and then, after each of the first meetings, he repeated his account of Isme's discomfort. A few of the women in the group would linger to listen to Davi's repetition of Isme's complaints, beaming with pleasure at this demonstration of marital devotion. It was clear that, although Davi must have consciously pampered Isme before she developed insomnia, this, to him, was more than simple pampering—her sleeplessness distressed him deeply, and was the source of serious concern.

We decided that Isme had probably developed a sleep pattern that, for a large portion of the night, drifted between sleep and waking. But Davi, like Isme, could not accept that explanation, nor would they accept the methods we suggested to counteract her frequent, brief arousals. There, of course, lay our difficulty—Isme would not concede that she drifted into sleep even briefly—she was awake, all the time, and she knew this as an absolute certainty. We proposed to both of them that Isme undergo examination at a hospital sleep clinic, but they protested that Isme had seen many doctors and undergone numerous examinations. It was useless to explain that the examination we were now recommending in no way resembled any previous medical examination Isme had encountered, just as it was useless to explain that no one exists completely without sleep. We began to despair of ever helping Isme to help herself, and we were not too surprised when one night she failed to attend the group meeting. We soon learned, however, that her absence was related to an event which had nothing to do with her sleep therapy. Another full week passed before Isme telephoned. Her voice sounded weak with sadness. Davi was hospitalized, she explained. A heart attack. We asked her to come in at once.

When Isme sat down to speak with us, we noticed how her bearing had changed. Her shoulders had narrowed, her eyes were downcast. From her fragmented, broken description, we pieced together the events that led to Davi's heart attack.

It was a dark, dreary night. Gusts of wind blew through the evergreens, setting in motion the creaking bare branches of the maples behind the house. Intermittently, a loose pane in the window across the hall rattled briefly. Davi awakened. He thought he heard a key in the door downstairs. No, he said to himself, it was the wind. But then he heard the faintest squeak of the stairs, as if someone was gingerly climbing the steps. Now his heart was pounding, and his mouth felt dry. Then he observed on the wall opposite his open door, a faint circle of light skimming back and forth. The light hesitated a moment, then seemed to snap itself off. Davi's heart thumped once.

The clear silhouette of a man stood outlined in the hall. Davi lay quite still. The silhouette entered the room, hesitated, waited, then receded ever so gently. Davi half-closed his eyes, so that he might appear to be asleep, but would still be able to see. Now the silhouette slipped silently forward again, sidling to the dresser, swiftly sliding open one of the drawers, and quickly all of the drawers, now rummaging, still swift and still silent, plucking objects from the drawers and thrusting them into a bag he held in his hand. Davi tried to keep his breathing constant and even, as if he were sleeping. Inadvertently, he caught his breath. The silhouette stopped, straightened, glanced about the room, shifting his head to each corner rapidly, after which, satisfied, he returned to the drawers. Davi saw the shadowed arm reach out along the dresser top and snatch the wallet lying there. Now the silhouette paused once again, and then retreated softly from the room and along the hallway until, reaching the stairs, it creaked gingerly down the steps. The wind muffled the sound of retreating footsteps. Davi did not hear the front door close. Uncertain whether the silhouette had actually departed, or might still return, Davi lay still for an aeon, until finally he heard the motor of an automobile turn over, and then fade as the vehicle sped away. He had raised himself in bed to start toward the window, when a sharp pain stabbed his shoulder blade and ripped across his chest. Davi fell back.

"Isme," he called.

"Davi," she answered softly.

"Are you awake?" he asked.

"Always," she answered.

"Then you saw?"

"You moaned," she said in Arabic. "Are you sick?"

"You saw," he repeated.

"What is the matter? Saw what?"

"The light," he mumbled, snapping on the lamp and reaching for the phone on the night table beside the bed. He dialed O, and, still speaking Arabic, asked for an ambulance.

Isme, observing the whiteness in his face, snatched the phone from his hand and, her panic growing, somehow got through, with all her broken English, to a hospital, and then the police.

Only then, with Davi lying back and breathing heavily, did Isme look around the room. The dresser drawers were open, all of them. Shirts, sweaters, undergarments, hose were strewn about the floor.

As she sat there, absolutely stunned, comprehension seeped through. Slowly, she understood—someone had rifled the room. But her comprehension extended deeper than this. With a burglary in progress, Isme had been fast asleep!

Some weeks later, Isme sat opposite us again, her eyes downcast.

"Do you sleep now?" we asked.

"I get out of bed," she answered sheepishly.

Isme had taken the one giant step forward. She was dealing rationally with the problem of sleep.

The causes of hyperlixia are, for all their convolution, clear enough. Amazing as it may seem, problem sleepers who suffer hyperlixia are actually victims of *too much sleep*, taking into consideration not only their nighttime sleep, but the frequent moments of sleep they steal during daylight hours as well. Remember that we have defined hyperlixia as an excessive amount of light sleep, and when the body is offered extra sleep, which is to say more sleep than the body actually requires, that extra sleep almost invariably falls into Stage 1 light sleep. The difficulty arises because during the night the excessive amounts of light sleep are confused by the sleeper with wakefulness. Alternatively, the sleeper may develop a sleep pattern that oscillates between Stages 0, 1, and 2, without reaching 3 and 4 deep sleep. In these fluctuations, the sleeper remembers the wakeful moments and forgets the interim periods of sleep. Thus, while he is firmly convinced he is not sleeping enough, in point of fact he is actually sleeping too much, taking into account his daytime naps.

The underlying obstacle to fighting hyperlixia rests in the identification of the problem. This is the crucial first step to a cure. If you spend long periods in bed at night, presumably awake, you must follow all procedures specified for hyperlixia, regardless of your absolute certainty that you are awake all the time. It is this certainty that you are awake which lies at the root of your difficulty, and the hyperlixia prescripts are designed to give you an insight into the source of your distress.

Our goal in the treatment of hyperlixia is to decrease the proportion of sleep spent in the restless, light sleep stages by imposing conditions that will lead to a deeper, more restful sleep.

Prescripts and Proscripts for Hyperlixia

• You are now aware how easily sleep and wakefulness are confused. In order to remove the confusion, a new rule must be put into effect. All time spent lying down, whether or not sleep occurs, must be counted as sleep time.

Now, calculate your average total sleep time. Carefully include all time spent in bed, awake as well as asleep, all time spent in repose (on a chaise lounge or sofa, even though you may be awake for all of this time), plus all time spent dozing while seated. If your new total rises to a level which you consider should be satisfactory, but you nevertheless sustain a sleep problem, your disturbance probably lies in the quality of your sleep—you probably suffer hyperlixia.

Hyperlixia paradoxically often results from an excessive quantity of sleep. Before you dismiss the possibility of oversleeping, search your daily routine for smuggled packets of sleep. Do you doze during train rides or automobile trips? Do you rest without seeming to sleep? Do you spend part of your day or evening relaxing, while you daydream or listen to music? Do you doze for a few minutes in front of the television set? All of these moments add to your total sleep time, just as a handful of peanuts and a small slice of cheese add to your caloric intake. Just as nibbling destroys a diet and adds to your weight, hors d'oeuvres of sleep add to your total sleep time, and detract from the quality of your nighttime sleep. Sleep snacks must be eliminated. We have found that many people are fiercely protective of these stolen moments. They are unable, or unwilling, to give them up. That is fine. If you wish to sleep on a train or in an automobile, of course you may. But remember, if you suffer light sleep at night your own natural sleep pattern was altered by your daytime naps, and the choice was yours. We need only state the obvious: uninterrupted sleep is far more satisfying than intermittent snatches. If continuous sleep in bed is your goal, you must circumvent sleep elsewhere.

• When riding in an automobile as a passenger, talk as much as possible.

• On a train, do a crossword puzzle, write a letter, prepare a shopping list. If you find yourself unable to stay awake, stand up. We appreciate that this suggestion is distasteful, but we hold firm; stand up! Even before you sit, if a little old lady tries to grab your seat, let her get away with it, remain standing. If you are a little old lady, give your seat to a man. The novelty of the situation will itself keep you awake. The principle is fundamental: if you carefully destroy clandestine sources of sleep, your nighttime sleep will be lengthened and deepened.

• When you awaken during the night, look at your clock. If you are awake after thirty minutes, you will, of course, get out of bed and follow the instructions that appear in the other prescripts and proscripts on this point. However, if you have made a sincere effort to get up, and have failed because your attempts to keep track of the time during the night have been unsuccessful, you must now follow this specific procedure. When you look at your clock, make a mental note of the exact time which will, after ten minutes have passed, appear on the clock. For example, if you awaken at 3:33 A.M., add ten minutes to make a mental note of 3:43, then try to look at the clock once more, at 3:43. You will quite likely find yourself consulting the clock at 3:34, at 3:35, perhaps again at 3:37, then possibly again at 3:39, and then finally, after a big chunk of time, at something like 4:36. When this happens, the lost time between 3:39 and 4:36 *was actually spent in sleep.* You may still feel, however, that you were awake during the entire period. If this is the case, you can now utilize a fascinating psychological finding. Your storehouse of ideas cannot accommodate two contradictory thoughts at the same time. When two mutually exclusive perceptions are registered, the perception which fills the weaker need must succumb. You can take advantage of the dissonance process to overwhelm and permanently banish your mistaken perception of wakefulness. You need merely reaffirm the logical conclusion that you must have been sleeping. The logic is supported by the face of the clock at which you are staring—if you were supposed to note 3:43, and you are looking at 4:36, the evidence is as overwhelming as the *denouement* in a detective story—you must have been asleep! Simply repeat silently, "I must have been asleep. I was sleeping. I had to be sleeping." At this point, you will sink into a deeper, more satisfying sleep. Moreover, as you repeat the formula on succeeding occasions, the misapprehension of wakefulness will permanently yield a portion of its strength to its stronger rival, logic. It will finally weaken to the extent that it will cease to plague you and you will enjoy a deeper, less troubled sleep.

• The best guarantee of deep sleep is a tired body. Muscle fatigue intrinsically induces sleep. In addition to the other soporific effects inherent in fatigue, the grateful relaxation of your weary muscles will lull you into a deep sleep. This phenomenon is one which we have all experienced so it requires no elaboration. It is supported, however, by parallels in physiology as well as by our daily observations. In neural activity, the activation of one neuron in a reverberatory chain will activate the entire chain, and will finally recruit participation of other, adjacent neurons. In a similar manner, the activation of one component of a response will recruit the other components of that response. The relaxation of your tired muscles in bed will recruit the other components of the sleep response to soothe you into a deep sleep.

• Begin an exercise program. Your first step is to gain clearance from your physician. Then select an activity which permits steady, brisk, sustained exertion. A sample of such activities includes: walking, jogging, running, cycling, swimming, tennis, handball, squash. Golf may be substituted, but only if it is played without a riding cart, and for at least double the time periods specified below.

Start your new regimen with at least thirty minutes of activity each day. If you are jogging, running, or swimming, your activity will need to be interspersed with less strenuous exertions. Running would be alternated with walking, for example. After one week, increase the total time period to forty-five minutes each day, and then, after the second week, increase the time period to one hour per day.

For the first two weeks, you must exercise every day. If you have chosen tennis, for example, and you cannot get a game every day, play when possible, and then walk or engage in another activity on free days. From the third week forward, you may cut your exercise down to four or five days per week.

• Exercise early in the day. The morning is preferable. Four o'clock in the afternoon is the cutoff hour. Be sure to exercise earlier. However, if early hours are impossible for you, experiment with the hour before your evening meal. This may yield satisfactory results for you. If you have chosen a competitive sport such as handball, tennis, or squash, evening participation is not advised. The competitive element may stimulate you sufficiently to counteract the fatigue. Therefore, if evening is your only available time, do not choose a competitive activity.

• Limit liquids after 6:00 P.M. It is permissible to drink one cup of tea or decaffeinated coffee at the end of your evening meal, but no more. The quantity individuals need to consume for comfort varies widely. Therefore, you will need to adjust your own liquid consumption, so that it drops below your present quantity, but still satisfies your bodily needs. Diminished liquid is necessary to eliminate sleep-disturbing bladder signals. Light sleep allows even faint messages to sneak through to rouse you into a waking state. Therefore, pressure may awaken you more than once during the night. The source of the alert, a distended bladder, is best avoided by the simple expedient of drinking less during the evening.

In summary:
• Eliminate all daytime naps, catnaps as well as full-fledged naps.
• Use conversation, puzzles, letter writing, and other strategies of your own choice to circumvent sleep during the day.
• When you awaken during the night, leave your bed after thirty minutes.
• If you cannot manage to leave your bed, look at your clock every ten minutes.
• If, in the process of tracking the passage of time, you fail to note a block of time, you must repeat silently, "I have been asleep." Continue this self-education process on subsequent nights.
• Engage in a regular program of vigorous activity.
• Limit liquids after 6:00 P.M.

CHAPTER 5

Pleisomnia

Pleisomnia, sleep which is interrupted by many awakenings during the night, often appears after age forty. As maturity develops, the total amount of Stage 4 sleep decreases, and the remaining Stage 4 sleep grows lighter. For older sleepers, the EEG still traces the typical roll of the delta wave, but the valleys are not as deep, the hills not as high, revealing the lighter Stage 4 sleep common in middle age. In Stage 4 sleep the man of fifty is not as difficult to rouse as the boy of fifteen. In the same manner, other sleep stages grow lighter with age. Most mature adults can recall the pangs inflicted by the alarm clock during their school years. Now, many years later, with the loss of deep sleep, their morning distress has been dissipated, but in its place they often discover the irritant of frequent awakenings during the night.

As a matter of fact, even when sleep is entirely satisfactory, the EEG shows a number of arousals every night at all ages past childhood. To be sure, these brief awakenings are not always recalled; the sleeper may remain unaware of any awakening at all. An average of two such awakenings occurs at age twenty. The number rises to four at age forty, and then to almost five at age seventy. The critical and troublesome change lies not in the number of these arousals, but in the duration of the wakeful periods. As they lengthen, the sleeper experiences the discomfort which accompanies the inability to fall back to sleep. Statistics reveal that as the number and duration of awakenings increase, so does the amount of time spent in bed. At middle age, people begin to stay in bed for a longer period each night, and here lies one exacerbating factor. It may be this very factor which contributes to your pleisomnia.

The broken sleep of pleisomnia is frequently attributed in older people to the aging process. An examination of sleep patterns from infancy to old age reveals broken sleep at both ends of the age scale, infancy as well as old age. A newborn infant sleeps in approximately six separate periods distributed through each twenty-four-hour day. After a year, sleep has consolidated into roughly three distinct periods; the night, plus one or two naps. The naps are relinquished by the time the child is ready to attend school. Thereafter, the unbroken block of sleep remains relatively stable through young adulthood to age forty. Then, in the forties, many adults, but not all by any means, find that they awaken one or more times. Finally, naps are often reintroduced after age sixty. An overview presents a picture which resembles the fabled seven stages of man, in which man regresses to a childlike condition in the later years. We believe the picture to be deceptive. The impression it conveys is false. We reject the concept that age and regression go hand in hand. The very supposition is a slander.

Naps and broken sleep at night are more closely related to social conditions than to the changes which accompany age. One critical social condition in this connection is the fact that retirement occurs shortly after age sixty. It is as logical to attribute after-sixty naps, when they occur, to newly acquired free time as to attribute them to advancing years. Moreover, studies find that there are numbers of people in their seventies who never doze or nap. All of this supports the thesis that the aging process, *per se*, is not necessarily the sole underlying cause of the naps of the elderly. Additional support is furnished by the observation that in the siesta countries the afternoon nap is a custom of the young as well as the old. It may be posited that in our country the nap would also be a habit for the young, but because of the demands of the working years, it is concentrated here in older people.

It seems to us that other, more pernicious social conditions also contribute to the resumption of what appears to be the childlike sleep pattern of the aged in this country. It is entirely possible that if young people suffered the conditions of their elders—retirement, reduction of responsibility, inactivity, withdrawal of respect, diminished esteem—then even the young would seek escape from this onerous social climate by acquiring the habit of a brief nap or two during the day. For many of the elderly, nighttime awakenings result not simply from lighter sleep during the night, but also from the excessive quantity of sleep accumulated in habitual daytime naps.

The approaching 1980s hold the promise of "gray power," an assertion of the rights of a persecuted minority—the aged. If you are surprised to see elderly people referred to as a persecuted minority, your very unfamiliarity with the myriad slurs and slights born by older individuals emphasizes the need for affirmative action on their part. The single word *old* applied to a man or to a woman conveys without further elaboration, a world of indignity. Who would wish to seek advice from a woman characterized as "old"? Who would relish an evening spent with an "old" man? It is of course possible for some to overcome this massive and oppressive prejudice, but this can be accomplished only by the superior force of prestige, power, or other attributes, like exceptional charm or unusual wealth, and even then the individual becomes "old *but* wise" or "old *but* charming." Never is the description phrased "old *and* wise" or "old *and* charming" and, significantly, the word *old* is invariably included in the description.

Hopefully, those of advancing age who are sensitized will take their place beside the other minorities and claim an equal share of respect and opportunity. When the movement for gray power fulfills its promise and becomes a reality, when social inequities based on age have been erased, perhaps we will be in a position to assess accurately the contribution of age *per se* to pleisomnia.

Some young people are also victimized by pleisomnia. Many of them are suffering depression. It is much easier to tell your physician or your friends that you cannot sleep than to report that you are intensely depressed. The sleepless condition evokes sympathy. Depression, on the other hand, frequently elicits a pep talk or a sermon, neither of which serves to lift the sadness. Many people do not even realize that they are depressed. Some have been prey to depression all of their lives, and are consequently unable to refer to a standard of comparison. They cannot compare their present mood to the serenity of another time, because they never were serene. You are undoubtedly acquainted with men and women who suffer chronic depression. You can recognize them by a peculiarly flat, emotionless tone of voice. They typically reflect little if any facial animation. They seem to walk through their daily routines, and even through their leisure activities, in mechanical fashion. Some of these unhappy people manifest their dejection in failure to sleep through the night.

In the earlier years, between twenty and fifty, physical differences are found between the good sleeper and the poor sleeper. Faster pulse rate and higher body temperature during both sleep and waking periods distinguish the poor sleeper. On the basis of a study at a Chicago sleep laboratory, poor sleepers register an average temperature of 98 degrees during the day and 97.6 during sleep. Good sleepers, by contrast, show a day temperature of 97.9, which drops at night to 97.2. These differences are not as small as they may seem, when one considers that the entire range of body temperatures spans less than ten degrees. The timing of the rise and fall of temperature also differs between those who sleep well and those who do not. Toward morning, the temperature of the sound sleeper starts to climb back to the daytime level while the temperature of the poor sleeper continues to decline. Poor sleepers are more restless; they turn and change positions frequently. Poor sleepers also exhaust their entire store of deep sleep early in the night, so that after the first half of the night, all their sleep is light. They spend considerably less time in dream sleep than do people who sleep restfully.

In the same Chicago study, other traits also distinguished the poor sleeper from the good sleeper. Minor physical discomforts plagued those who complained of insomnia. They scored high in affirmative answers on questions which dealt with dizziness, headaches, blurred vision, colds, and various additional aches and pains. Their responses to a battery of questions revealed them to be troubled by insecurities: difficulty in reaching decisions, anxiety, and self-doubt were reflected. The results indicate that sleep disturbances and general discomfort are close companions.

Pleisomnia has been attributed to a disturbance of the circadian cycle. Some subjects tested in sleep experiments revealed atypical variations in other functions as well as prolonged arousals during the night. A number of physical processes vary routinely with the time of day or night. Body temperature, for example, reaches a peak in the middle of the day for most people, and falls to a low point between two o'clock and five o'clock in the early morning. Heart rate, blood pressure, blood cell count, metabolism, volume of urine, and other functions also rise and fall with regularity within each twenty-four-hour period. Indices of these functions in victims of pleisomnia showed patterns of variation which differed from the patterns of good sleepers. It seems that many a pleisomniac marches to the tick of a different clock. Additionally, the records of sleep-test subjects who awaken frequently reveal that the progression of sleep stages fails to follow the usual pattern. Stage 4 sleep for these subjects, if it occurs at all, is minimal, and dream sleep is diminished.

These observations, like most answers in the search for information, pose a new set of questions. We do not know whether 1) the unusual body rhythms of the subject cause the frequent awakenings; or 2) the frequent awakenings cause the unusual body rhythms; or 3) both the frequent awakenings and the unusual body rhythms are caused by some unknown third factor. In order to deal with your pleisomnia, we will proceed on the basis of a practical decision. We will assume that your frequent awakenings are autonomous and that your sleep disturbance controls your other unusual body rhythms. We will therefore recommend measures to encourage Stage 4 deep sleep. To accomplish this, you will be required to adjust your sleep schedule, an adjustment which, because it is uncomfortable, will be applied in gradual stages, in order to ease the transition for you.

If, like the subjects in these studies, you suffer from general discomfort and insecurity, you should give some thought to your personal emotional adjustment. In any case, you must take measures to encourage deep sleep. You must practice Somniant Techniques assiduously to foster relaxation. You must also work on your personal emotional adjustment.

Your sleep-related habits will play an important role in determining whether you awaken frequently during the night. If you reward awakening, the tendency to awaken again will gain strength. If, upon waking, you comfort yourself with food, drink, entertainment, or anything else which is pleasant, you will be sacrificing future sleep for a moment of pleasure. Your body, like a spoiled child, will certainly wake up and demand a reward again on another night.

When this point was explained at a seminar, one participant confessed that occasionally, when desperate, he allowed himself the pleasure of a glass of cream sherry—but only occasionally, he added, in mitigation of his transgression. Ironically, an occasional reward creates a stronger habit than constant and continuous reward. When B. F. Skinner studied habitual behavior, he found that habits which were followed by reward every now and then were more resistant to extinction than habits followed by reward each and every time they were practiced. The habit of gambling is an interesting case in point. It is well known that gambling behavior is one of the most difficult of all behaviors to extinguish. In gambling, the win, the payoff, is, of course, the reward, and it is clear that even the best of gamblers win on a highly irregular basis. They neither expect nor receive the reward of winning on every single bet. Within the Skinnerian framework, the strength and persistence of the habit of gambling are directly related to the irregular pattern of wins and losses inherent in gambling.

Skinner's experiments were performed with animals who were trained to press a bar for a pellet of food. The bar-press was the habit: the pellet was the reward. Some of the animals received a pellet each time the bar was pressed. Others were given the food pellet on an irregular basis, in a procedure similar to that of the gentleman who drank his sherry only occasionally, and the gambler who, like all gamblers, wins only intermittently.

The results of the experiment showed that intermittent reward established a stronger habit than did continuous reward. You may have noticed the same phenomenon operating in your own behavior. Consider the mechanical action of starting the motor of your automobile. Turning the ignition key is your habit. The running sound of the motor is the reward. If your motor has started immediately every time you turned the key, and then one day it fails to start, you would undoubtedly still try to start the motor, but probably for only a limited time before you gave up and telephoned a service station. On the other hand, if your motor had often failed to start when you turned the ignition key for the first time, your efforts to start the motor would continue much longer before you finally yielded. Your key-turn habit would persist for a longer period if it had previously been rewarded on an occasional basis. This phenomenon—the development of a stronger habit through intermittent, as opposed to constant, reward—can be supported in terms of simple logic. If your motor always started regularly, its failure to start now reveals that something is wrong, and so you call the mechanic with reasonable promptness. But if failure of the motor to start immediately was common in the past, you would continue to turn the key for a much longer period of time, in the expectation that ultimately, exactly as in the past, the motor will catch. Skinner, in his studies, never reported any of his discoveries in terms of reasons for the behavior. He simply reported results, and Skinner's results have yielded rules of behavior which are now accepted in the scientific community.

In terms of insomnia and starting your car, the reactions involved when you activate the motor of your automobile differ in a number of respects from your reactions when you awaken during the night, but both responses represent behavior, and are therefore subject to the same principles. These principles establish that, while a steady reward for awakening will lead to a continuation of that habit, an intermittent reward for the same behavior will lead to an even stronger tendency to awaken.

Myron, who humorously referred to himself as the banana man, combined several elements which nourish pleisomnia when he engaged in his nightly excursions to a stemmed crystal bowl on a table in the den of his home. Betty, Myron's wife, kept the bowl filled at all times with unblemished peaches, polished red apples, occasional clusters of glistening grapes, and, most important of all, and selected especially for Myron, one single and perfect banana, its yellow skin flecked with small brown freckles. She was careful to make certain that Myron's banana was at the peak of its sweetness, the flesh still firm, the fruity scent ready to waft out the moment the skin was peeled away. It was Betty's custom, every Monday and Friday, to check the refrigerator before she made up her shopping list so that an adequate supply of bananas was always ensured. Then, every evening after dinner Betty would take a banana either out of the refrigerator or from the kitchen counter and place it in the stemmed crystal bowl of fruit on the table in the den.

Myron was a pleasant man to live with. He was exceptionally successful financially, he was esteemed in the community as a result of his generous contributions to charitable causes, and he was delightfully amusing. He could relate an ordinary incident in such a way that it became hilariously funny. Myron loved to make people laugh. Almost every evening, he would entertain Betty with witty accounts of trivial events at his office. He was unreasonable in only one area—and that area was so small and circumscribed that Betty found it easy to humor him without protest.

The house was dark. On the night table, the illuminated face of the digital clock read 3:01. Myron sighed in his sleep, turned over, and then opened his eyes. He sighed automatically once again and lay still, allowing wakefulness to flow into all the recesses of his mind. Oh, yes, it was time, it must be time. In a moment, he would look at the clock, but first a few more moments of rest. In less than a minute—he could wait no longer—he leaned on his elbow and swung his feet to the floor, brushing against his slippers at the side of his bed. He slid his feet into the slippers and then, keeping his hand against the wall to guide himself, he padded slowly out of the bedroom and down the hall to the entrance foyer, where he snapped on the ceiling chandelier. He stepped down into the den, four steps below the level of the foyer, and he reached out and lit the antique Bristol lamp. Then, taking just one step toward the crystal bowl, he stopped abruptly in surprise. For almost one full minute, Myron stared at the bowl, unable to comprehend. When finally he absorbed the full impact of what he saw, he turned and hurried to the kitchen, where he opened the refrigerator and searched it methodically, moving bowls and plastic containers aside to examine the corners of each of the shelves. Finally, the worst of his fears was confirmed. Myron slammed the refrigerator door and returned to the den. Gloomily, he picked a peach from the bowl, reached for a paper napkin on the table, and stood there, biting thoughtfully into the peach.

Careful not to allow the juice to drip onto his pajamas, Myron wondered what possible earthshaking assignment could have prevented Betty from doing this one small, little, tiny favor for him. How much effort, after all, would it take? One simple word to the fruit man, that's all that was required. In an entire long and idle, empty day, with absolutely no obligation to do anything other than pamper herself, all that he asked was one small thought about his comfort. All day long, while he argued with union delegates, while he negotiated with avaricious commission agents, and screamed at the idiots at the air-freight terminal, what did she have to do? Her picayune concerns were more important than his welfare, he mused bitterly. While he wore himself out trying to cajole the high-priced engineer into producing a new product, she amused herself by buying Italian dresses, French shoes, and Spanish nightgowns. Seventy-two dollars for a nightgown, he reflected bitterly, and not even one spare moment to think of him. He looked at the peach pit and then, deliberately, he threw it to the floor. It landed under the table, rolling to a stop on the cream-colored section of the Indian rug. Good, he thought, let it stay right there. He turned and strode back upstairs into the bedroom, where he snapped on the main switch, lighting all the lamps at once.

"Betty!" he shouted. "Where the hell is my banana?"

She bolted upright in bed, still half-asleep. "What happened?" she screamed in fright. "Myron, what is it?"

"Where is it?" he shouted again. "Where is it? In the fruit store, that's where it is," he thundered.

Betty put her head in her hands. "Oh, my God," she moaned. "I forgot. I forgot all about your banana."

Myron's behavior revealed two separate difficulties which he had inadvertently linked together. First, he sustained a need which had fixated upon a banana. Second, he used the same nightly banana both to satisfy that need and to reward his habit of awakening during the night. When Myron told us this story, his good-natured humor failed to conceal his intense reaction to the frustration of his nocturnal ritual. We decided to proceed slowly. First, Myron would modify the hour of his nightly awakening, and then, upon completion of this first assignment, he would begin gently to vary his need for a banana. We devised a schedule for Myron. We determined that he always awakened shortly after three o'clock in the morning. Our initial objective was to gradually move this time back, closer to the time he had fallen asleep, so that eventually he would not awaken for the banana at all. His schedule ran as follows:

1st Week	For 7 nights, set alarm for 2:30 A.M. Eat banana.
2nd Week	For 7 nights, set alarm for 2:00 A.M. Eat banana.
3rd Week	For 7 nights, set alarm for 1:30 A.M. Eat banana.
4th Week	For 7 nights, set alarm for 1:00 A.M. Eat banana.

5th Week	For 7 nights, set alarm for 12:30 A.M. Eat banana.
6th Week	For 7 nights, set alarm for midnight. Eat banana.
7th Week	For 7 nights, do not set alarm at all, and before retiring eat banana.

Myron encountered a roadblock the very first week. The alarm clock, with its new wakening time, interfered with the natural progression of his habit, so that now he did not fall asleep readily after eating the banana. Consequently, he was frustrated, an intolerable condition for Myron. He abandoned the entire schedule.

A few months later, Myron traveled to Houston on a business trip. His engineer accompanied him. Before he departed, Betty wrapped two bananas in plastic bags and placed them in a shoe box in Myron's valise. He was scheduled to return to his own home on the third night. When the two men arrived in Houston, they found that the hotel had lost their reservations. No room was available. They spent an hour telephoning other hotels without success. The city was filled to the last room. Myron marched back to the reception desk, and finally, after much discussion, which included some show of temper from the usually placid Myron, the manager succeeded in locating one room for both men. They rode up in the elevator, triumphant. In the room, Myron tipped the porter generously, started to open his bag, and, spying the shoe box, abruptly remembered the two bananas. Out of the corner of his eye, he glanced at the engineer. This man, with his M.I.T. degree and his huge fees, had always intimidated Myron. He could envision the faint smile of amusement the engineer would register when he spotted the bananas. He might even mention the bananas to the other men. They would all smile. Probably laugh aloud. The engineer stepped into the bathroom. Stealthily, quickly, Myron opened his valise, extracted the shoe box, and then opened the door of the room. Luckily, the chambermaid was standing at the end of the corridor beside her rolling cart. He flew down the hall and handed the box to the startled chambermaid, mumbling a few muffled words about throwing the box away, as he pressed a dollar bill into her hand.

Each night at the hotel, he awakened shortly after three o'clock in the morning. Each night, without his banana, he was unable to remain asleep for more than a fifteen- or twenty-minute period. Each night he lay awake for most of the night, feeling utterly miserable. At seven o'clock each morning, he dressed quietly so that he would not disturb the engineer, and walked downstairs to the hotel lobby, where he waited until the dining room opened for breakfast.

Laboriously, painfully, Myron finally succeeded in eliminating his nightly awakening by eating his banana earlier and earlier during the night, until at last he ate the banana before retiring. The second half of Myron's schedule was now planned to overcome his need for a banana. We wanted to help him generalize so that a variety of foods would serve to placate his peculiar hunger. In order to transfer the magnetism of the banana to some other food, that food was paired with the banana in Pavlovian fashion. Pavlov paired a buzzer with food, so that in time the buzzer alone elicited salivation. Utilizing the same theory, the following schedule was designed to allow another food to satisfy Myron at night:

8th Week	For 7 nights, before retiring eat one banana, plus ½ chocolate eclair.
9th Week	For 7 nights, before retiring eat ½ banana, plus one chocolate eclair.
10th Week	For 7 nights, before retiring eat ¼ banana, plus one chocolate eclair.
11th Week	For 7 nights, before retiring eat one chocolate eclair.
12th Week	For 7 nights, before retiring eat one eclair, plus ½ dish of ice cream.
13th Week	For 7 nights, before retiring eat ½ eclair, plus one dish of ice cream.
14th Week	For 7 nights, before retiring eat ¼ eclair, plus one dish of ice cream.
15th Week	For 7 nights, before retiring eat one dish of ice cream.

Myron, trying to follow an unusual schedule designed for his own individual and unusual sleep-related behavior, exhibited a particularly low tolerance for self-induced frustration. He took two steps forward and one step backward. But if and when he ever finds himself ready to complete the pairing technique, and to follow the schedule scrupulously, he will liberate himself from the dictatorship of the banana. Myron's difficulties with behavior modification, as well as your own, will be considered further in our prescripts and proscripts.

Reward (Myron's banana) is not always a factor in cases of pleisomnia. We observed still another element in other individuals. Some victims behaved as if a sensitive alarm system had been set to receive every possible signal during the night. Most of us, while awake, are reasonably alert to various signals: the smell of smoke, the sound of footsteps in an empty house, a knock at the door, rain falling on a window pane, a change in temperature, and any number of others. When we go to sleep, we automatically turn off our receptive apparatus. We may then, if we wish, set our figurative alarm system, the reticular activating system of the brain, to awaken us to any given signal we specify. Most of us specify no signal at all. By contrast, some victims of pleisomnia fail to turn off their receptive apparatus, and consequently they receive signals with almost as much sensitivity at night as during the day. They wake to faint whispers of sound: the sigh of a heating system, the creak of floorboards settling into the foundation of a building, a breeze rustling a window shade, the chirp of a cricket, a distant siren, the slam of an automobile door, any sound at all. These people seem as vigilant as a fugitive with blood hounds close at hand. They behave as if they are afraid.

Gerald was typical of the fearful pleisomniac. He was a thin, tense young man who responded to friendly remarks with nervous laughter. He was apparently a skillful skier. Whenever he discussed skiing, his tense mannerisms disappeared, and he assumed a relaxed, easygoing personality. At other times, he appeared ill at ease. By his own estimate, he awakened at least fifteen times every night. At one group meeting, Gerald supplied the key to his pleisomnia. We were discussing the onset of insomnia, and each participant spoke of the earliest recollection of an inability to sleep. Gerald described a portion of his childhood. His father taught art at a New England college. As a child, Gerald shared a bedroom with his brother, who was three years older. Both of the boys, as well as two older sisters, experimented casually in various art media: watercolor, charcoal, oil, wood carving, and whatever else was available in school and at home.

One night, when Gerald was nine years old, his brother proudly placed on permanent exhibition, on the bureau in their common bedroom, his own clay model of the head of Mozart, copied from a picture in a book. To Gerald, nine years old, the model was terrifying. It represented not a bust on a pedestal but the head of a man severed from his trunk. As Gerald drifted off to sleep, he imagined that the head would shortly burst into life and would then pursue its own ghastly midnight business. He awakened periodically during the night in intense fear. Gerald's recollection of the evolution of his fear was dim. He recalled that, in time, he became accustomed to the head standing on the bureau. The memory of how and when it disappeared was lost to him. Further exploration revealed to Gerald that his extreme nighttime vigilance began with his early terror of the bust of Mozart. His sleep had been paired with fear, and because of the pairing, the fear persisted even after the original threat disappeared. The unremitting fear resulted in an overwhelming need to monitor his environment throughout the night, thus accounting for Gerald's fifteen awakenings.

Gerald's case was unique, and a number of ingredients contributed to the survival of his fear of the night. Gerald's condition, however, resembles a more common problem which may also manifest itself in oversensitized vigilance at night, the fear of death (see Chapter Seven). If your frequent awakenings occur in response to minor variations in background stimulation, if you awaken to a slight sound or at a small provocation, then you must investigate the possibility that you are suffering some kind of fear in the night, and you must treat your frequent awakenings as a form of fear response which requires an extinction procedure. Because the feared object differs so widely from one person to another, it is not possible to give a general set of prescripts and proscripts. However, the mere discovery of fear as a contributing factor constitutes a significant step along the road to better sleep.

As we have already indicated, in addition to fear, still another emotion may contribute to pleisomnia. Chronic anger may boil over several times each night to awaken a pleisomniac, who then must contend with a double discomfort: anger plus sleep disturbance. Lena's pleisomnia is an example. She was born in Newfoundland off the coast of Canada of European parents who emigrated to Canada to seek a better life. But life still proved difficult for the family of six, who, hungry in Europe, found little more of the necessities, and none of the luxuries, in Canada. However, Lena explained, she knew of no condition other than poverty, and was therefore content as a child. When Lena was fourteen, her mother died. As the oldest daughter, she was expected to assume the household duties as well as to attend school. She washed the laundry, cleaned the house, and cooked the meals before and after school. But the heaviest burden of all involved rearing the youngest child, a boy of four, who clung desperately to Lena when she, a child herself, yearned to play with her schoolmates. Lena took care of her little brother, and inside she was angry. Anger became a part of Lena. She lived in resentment. As a girl in her teens, she slept with anger. In later years, as a young wife, as a mother, and as a grandmother, she was always devoted, always loving, always giving—and always angry. But now a new component was introduced. The quality of her sleep grew lighter with the years, thereby enabling Lena's anger, which remained as a habitual response to each frustration the day presented, to bubble over intermittently every night, awakening Lena at each overflow.

Lena's mission was twofold. First, she needed to find outlets through which to discharge her emotions during the day. Her second assignment involved measures to deepen the quality of her sleep. Lena's two correctives will be described in the prescripts and proscripts at the end of this chapter.

The eight-hour myth, which causes so much trouble in other forms of insomnia, also appears in cases of pleisomnia. Many individuals are unaware of the average hours of sleep at various ages. They are misled by their expectation of eight hours, and therefore expect more sleep than their biological systems can accommodate. When people who harbor unrealistic expectations for sleep lie in bed too long, they naturally doze and awaken frequently. These frequent awakenings are demands issued by their bodies, not for sleep, but for activity. We tend to consider sleep as a necessity for health, and exertion as optional. In this situation, quite the opposite is the case. For someone who is trying to sleep for a longer period than is biologically appropriate for his or her age, exertion, rather than sleep, is the necessity for health. Remember that the proverbial eight hours of sleep is a myth, and it does not apply to you, or to anyone. A recent statistic reveals the national sleep average to be seven and one-half hours per night. At age forty, this seven and one-half-hour average starts to decline. At age sixty-five and over, it dips to six and one-half hours, and even less. These are average figures. Half of the individuals within each average sleep less than the average amount. As a problem sleeper, you should aim for less than the quantity of sleep noted in your age group.

Recently, we visited an elderly relative, a cherished aunt who prefers to report her age as seventy-nine. She greeted us eagerly, explaining almost as soon as we entered the door that she had a sleep problem. She awakened frequently during the night. When we asked the time she retired, she shook her head sadly. "Not until eleven-thirty at the earliest," she answered with an air of virtue.

"When do you wake up?" we asked.

"At seven, but I stay in bed until eight."

"That's a good night's sleep," we pointed out. "Almost nine hours in bed. Why don't you get out of bed at seven? That would help you with your problem."

Aunt Lillian appeared hurt. "What would I do at seven?" she asked in an injured tone.

"You could cook, or bake."

"For whom?" she asked. Aunt Lillian is a widow. She has children and grandchildren, but she lives alone.

"Do you like to sew?"

"Don't you remember the arthritis in my fingers?"

"You could read."

"I do read. I read for hours every day." She shook her head. "You don't understand," she explained. "There's nothing to do when I get out of bed. I'm so bored."

"We do understand, Aunt Lillian. We understand completely. But your problem is not a problem of sleep."

Prescripts and Proscripts for Pleisomnia

• The basic general rule which applies to all types of insomnia is particularly applicable to pleisomnia. Each time you awaken during the night, you must, after thirty minutes awake, get out of bed. Once out of bed, you should occupy yourself with a dull or repetitive task like record keeping or needle work. Return to bed only when you are ready to fall asleep. If you are uncertain as to when you are "ready" to fall asleep, the Back-to-Bed Guide will be helpful.

• In order to consolidate your sleep into one solid block of time, you must first deprive yourself of sleep. You must go to bed so hungry for sleep that your sleep mechanism will rebel at arousal.

Retire at your usual time every night, but set your morning alarm one full hour earlier than its present setting. Get out of bed immediately when your alarm sounds. Absolutely no afternoon naps, of course. Continue this abbreviated sleep schedule until arousals decrease in number and diminish in duration. If after one week you do not see an improvement, you must then subtract one additional half hour from your total sleep time. Your sleep span should not exceed six hours per night. Continue this second abbreviated sleep schedule until your sleep pattern improves, which should happen in two to three weeks, providing you have not cheated and have followed this directive scrupulously.

When you find yourself sleeping more comfortably, you may then set your alarm fifteen minutes later for one week, thus restoring one quarter of an hour to your sleep time. Add on an additional fifteen minutes each week, until you have restored one hour. If, at any time, you again experience extended arousals, you must retreat to your last satisfactory sleep span.

• Physical activity is of the utmost importance in the quest for unbroken sleep. With the permission of your physician, start an exercise program. Choose an activity which you find pleasant, or at least tolerable. Strenuous exertion is excellent, if it is acceptable to you. The activity you select must be one in which you can engage every day. If your first choice is a weekend sport like skiing, for example, then you must supplement that sport with another activity during the week. Long walks, involving no expense at all, are obviously the most widely available activity, and a good long walk is a salutary exercise. If walking is your choice, you must not stroll. Maintain a fast pace, fast enough to leave you tired.

Begin with thirty minutes of exercise daily and increase the time to one hour. If, because of a physical disability, thirty minutes is too taxing for you, you may start with a shorter period, and increase that period up to your personal maximum. But even if you experience as many problems as Aunt Lillian, you must nevertheless engage in exercise every day. Your activity should be completed before 4 P.M. You may skip one or two days each week after you have been exercising for several weeks—but do not skip activity during the initial weeks of exercise.

• Studies have revealed that poor sleepers dream less than good sleepers. Restful sleep is characterized by high dream levels. Other studies have shown that it is possible to increase your own dream time. Your objective is to prolong the time you spend in dreams.

Each night, when you get into bed, think about a pleasant dream. Choose a locale, a cast of characters, and a plot for a dream which you would enjoy. Each morning, try to recall your dreams of the night. The mere fact that you think about dreams will encourage dreaming. You will not, of course, know whether you have increased your dream-sleep time. The success of your experiment will lie in the ultimate attainment of a more restful sleep. You will recognize success in a sense of well-being.

• This is the time to give some thought to possible underlying causes. Is anger disrupting your sleep? This is a determination which only you can make. Even if we worked together, and if, in our opinion, you were experiencing chronic anger, we would not inform you of our conclusion. If we did, you would turn your anger toward us without accepting our opinion. You must reach a conclusion about your anger, if it is warranted, by yourself. If you should decide that anger plays a part in your frequent awakenings, you would do well to discharge some of that anger.

Exercise is an excellent medium of discharge. The form of physical exercise you select should include an outlet for emotional effusion. The opportunity to slam a ball, as in tennis, golf, or handball, will permit you to drain off excess emotion. In the house, beating a rug offers a similar opportunity. Dances which include sudden, sharp movement are equally useful. If it is at all possible, choose this type of activity as your daily exercise. If such a choice is impossible for you, supplement your exercise with a form of forceful, explosive activity of the type just mentioned. You must engage in this activity until you feel slightly breathless every day. If you choose to beat a rug, only a few minutes will tire you and leave you breathless. If you dance, a longer period of time will be necessary.

In any case, remember that even if you are not angry, tennis, golf, handball, dancing, beating a rug, as well as any other stimulating exercise, will prove of enormous assistance in your quest for better sleep.

In summary:
- Do not remain in bed awake for more than thirty minutes.
- Return to bed only when you feel ready to sleep.
- Retire at your usual time.
- Set your alarm for one hour earlier than its present setting and get out of bed promptly when it rings.
- If, after one week, you do not experience marked improvement, subtract an additional half hour.
- When you find yourself awakening less frequently, you may restore your lost sleep time by moving your alarm ahead fifteen minutes each week.
- Start a program of vigorous exercise and follow it regularly.
- Think about pleasant dreams every night.
- Try to recall your dreams in the morning.
- Discharge anger in brief but forceful activity.

CHAPTER 6
Insomnia Turbula

Insomnia turbula is our term for sleep which is laden with uneasy dreams and therefore with an unpleasant emotional tone. It also describes sleep which is punctuated by nightmares. (A nightmare is distinguished from a troubled dream by its greater intensity and the element of an abrupt awakening.) If you suffer insomnia turbula, you can control your own dreams, and if you suffer recurrent nightmares, you can stop them. In several studies, college students have demonstrated that they could control, within limits, the duration of their dreams. They were able to dream for longer or shorter periods of time. Hospital patients under EEG observation can accurately indicate, by moving a finger while they are still sleeping, that a dream has begun. Additionally, many people, perhaps you yourself, have mastered the knack of awakening at a particular time or at a predetermined signal. With these simple skills as a basis, you can halt the turbulence which disrupts your sleep.

There are no statistics available to enable us to estimate the prevalence of nightmares in the general population. The literature of sleep is silent on this topic, except in the area of psychosis. We have encountered individuals who were clearly not psychotic, but who were nevertheless troubled by recurrent nightmares. One man in his fifties informed us that, although generally he fell asleep quickly, slept through the night, and awakened refreshed, nevertheless two or three times each week he was subjected to horror-filled dreams which awakened him with a shock. His dreams were so repugnant, their content so morbid, that he declined to furnish any of the details, except to say that in his nightmares those who were close to him, those whom he loved most dearly, suffered awful calamities. From the few random clues he supplied we surmised that in these recurrent nightmares he witnessed physical atrocities committed against his family. He would awaken abruptly after each nightmare, his heart pounding, unable to catch his breath. Sometimes, when he fell asleep again after the dream, the same story would continue, unfolding in the bizarre, disjointed fashion of dreams, a sequel to the frightening events of the earlier dream.

Recurrent dreams of a milder nature are common. Almost everyone can describe a repeated dream of his own. Frequently, these dreams are troubled, and they often suggest to the dreamer a particular frustration familiar during waking hours as well as in sleep. At a party we attended, in a large social group of professionals, three individuals separately described a repetitive dream, which, to the surprise of each of them, bore a remarkable resemblance to the recurrent dreams of the other two. The first to describe his dream, a shy, intelligent man, explained that invariably he found himself traveling via some strange and inappropriate means of transportation. For example, he would dream, over and over again, that he was riding an underground subway in a new and strange kind of train with seats suspended from the ceiling, in order to reach Paris from Des Moines, or some such unlikely starting point. After numerous repetitions, the dream would be followed by another similar dream, and in all of these dreams he was suffused with feelings of frustration and stress.

A second man interrupted to exclaim that the dream seemed almost a prelude to his own. In his recurring dream, he found himself walking in a strange place, where the streets, the shops, the buildings were all unfamiliar. The street signs were obscured by the branches of trees, or they were lost in shadows, or obliterated by weather and time. In the dream, he never thought to question the passersby, who were themselves absorbed in their own preoccupations, strangers passing on the streets. His dream too was permeated with apprehension and nagging fears: where was he, where were all the people he knew, how did he get here, would he ever return to his own world? The third member of the group, a woman who was employed by a public relations firm, described her own repetitive dream, a nightmare she had suffered for years. In her dream, she tried to keep an appointment for a meeting with someone at a particular place and time. It was important that she keep the appointment, but try as she might, she could never leave the house. One incident after another would detain her, bringing accumulating frustration as the clock ticked toward the appointed hour.

Each of these individuals, drawn from a homogeneous social group, dreamed of a destination and suffered the frustration of failing to achieve a goal. It is conceivable that, within the larger group also present at the social gathering that day, the others who did not contribute to the exchange all experienced similar dreams, or, on the contrary, that no one else in that group dreamed of goal frustration at all. Without knowledge of patterns of dreams, as well as of the people experiencing those dreams, and without additional knowledge of the frequency with which those dreams recur, we can know little about dreams as norms. Efforts to gather data concerning dreams were reported by Calvin Hall and R. L. Van der Castle in 1966 and by Fred Snyder in 1970, but these attempts merely touched the surface, and their results suffered from methodological defects. A psychotherapist who employs dreams as a yardstick against which to measure health or pathology is in a position similar to that of the therapists who dealt with so-called sexual deviancy before the Kinsey Report was issued. The therapist has no choice but to employ his or her own adjustment as a criterion.

As college students, we met Jean, a charming young woman who volunteered the information that she had recently been discharged from the Menninger Clinic, where, according to her account, she had perfected her bridge game, while emerging from what she conceived to be a mysterious psychotic state. She described one of her dreams in words so vivid that the dream still remains embedded in our memory. At the time of the dream she resided in Canada, where she had recently converted to Catholicism. In the dream, she stood outside a church in Quebec, looking up at a magnificent stained-glass window with a picture of the Three Wise Men under a star-studded sky. As she gazed at the window, the glass shuddered, and then a jagged crack opened from one side of the window to the other. From inside the church, through the crack in the window, a stream of blood poured out while she moaned in horror. Listening to the dream, we were shocked, and we reached the immediate conclusion that Jean's dream and her psychopathology comprised a single entity. Now, in retrospect, we question that early judgment. Although Jean was psychotic, we have no way of knowing how many normal people experience dreams of equivalent horror. We also realize now that, while the content of the nightmare seemed grandiose and far removed from the mundane, nevertheless, to this particular dreamer, that content was directly related to her daily activity of conversion ritual and church attendance.

We now take the position that in the absence of objective standards of comparison, dreams cannot offer, in and of themselves, adequate evidence of emotional illness. Often a diagnosis of psychosis is reached on the basis of other symptomology, and then the dreams which appear are adjudged to be disturbed because they are associated with the other symptoms. This second conclusion, the relationship of the dreams to the other symptoms, may or may not be valid, but the use of the dreams *per se* to diagnose psychosis is open to serious question. This suggests a salutary proscription. If, as we believe, a trained therapist cannot legitimately conclude that you suffer mental disorder because you experience certain kinds of nightmares, neither can you reach a similar judgment. If nightmares trouble you, your concern about their implications will only intensify your distress.

Uneasy dreams and troubled sleep often follow a personal loss or an unhappy situation. These dreams are expressions of grief. Some psychologists call all of the reactions to loss "the grief work," to convey the idea that emotion must be expressed in order to fade. In one case, a married woman who had ended a disastrous love affair suffered a period of depression. During sleep, she perspired so profusely that she would awaken with her nightgown soaking wet and with grooves on her palms where her clenched fists had pressed her fingernails into her hands. A social worker who had lost her satisfying position in a hospital and then obtained employment with a commercial firm under a demanding, obnoxious supervisor, reported turbulent dreams, along with aching jaws, which resulted from clamping her teeth together during sleep. A young woman whose baby was born impaired dreamed repeatedly that she was wandering about, alone, in an unfamiliar and lonely place where mist hung above the ground and the land was covered by tremendous rocks and leafless trees. These dreamers did not awaken precipitously as after a nightmare, nor were they frightened. However, they were experiencing a form of turbula, and it was clearly associated with trauma. In all of these cases, the uneasy dreams were relieved by the mere passage of time. If you are experiencing turbula as a reaction to a life situation, time will inevitably dull the edge of your pain. You must, however, make certain that you do not attempt to comfort yourself during this period with the types of rewards which will create an insomnia habit.

It is possible to find yourself troubled with the same type of distressful, unpleasant sleep even in the absence of a precipitating loss or tension factor. We call this *spontaneous turbula*, distinguished from *reactive turbula*, where the troubled dreams are a response to a life situation. In reactive turbula, intense emotions usually associated with loss or grief continue to exert pressure even through sleep. In spontaneous turbula, the source of the troubled dreams has not been established, but they may be the result of an automatic mechanical process. Our prescripts and proscripts will specify directions for dealing with each.

To the victim of insomnia turbula, beyond the immediate discomfort of the dreams themselves lies the lingering disturbance with regard to the import of the dreams. Along with fears of possible mental illness, which are not easily dismissed, rest other deeply rooted anxieties. Our literary, religious, social, and superstitious heritage ascribes meanings to dreams, meanings which we automatically absorb. Historically, dreams were accepted as precursors of coming events. Probably the most familiar predictive dream of all may be found in the Old Testament story of Joseph's interpretation of the Pharaoh's dream of seven fat kine followed by seven lean kine, who pounced upon their seven well-fed predecessors and devoured them. After Joseph explained to Pharaoh that the dream signified seven prosperous years followed by seven lean years, Pharaoh undertook to store his grain during the seven favorable years, thus averting the approaching seven-year famine, and Joseph thereby won fame and fortune. We can recall our own delighted childhood awe as we were struck by the significance of the dream, which, although mysterious, was simultaneously benign, in that it not only rescued Joseph from prison, but also saved the Pharaoh's subjects from starvation.

Some part of the same supernatural aura colors the aftereffect of the nightmare, without the benevolence inherent in the biblical dream. It is not uncommon for a dreamer to react to a dream as if it were predictive. Sometimes, in a time variation, the dreamer believes the event in his nightmare has already occurred. Many a long-distance telephone call is sparked by a dream of death or accident. In the millions of dreams which are recalled each day, some do, in fact, accurately reflect actual events, merely as the result of the laws of probability. At the same time that multitudinous dreams are transpiring, multitudinous events are taking place. On the basis of a random pairing of dreams and events, a number of them are certain to coincide. If you could observe a demonstration in which one million red cubes coded to represent specific events together with one million green cubes coded to represent dreams were all tossed into a huge drum, and then turned and mixed as in a gigantic state lottery, after which they were removed in pairs, one dream along with one event, you would witness the certainty with which a number of dreams would coincide with a corresponding event. Coincidence, not clairvoyance, would be the controlling factor.

If you survived the tedium of the myriad necessary draws, you would emerge from the exhibition with the objectivity of a Nobel Prize scientist, rejecting clairvoyance and recognizing coincidence. If, after all of that, you then went home to bed and dreamed that your cousin Alfred, whom you have not seen in years and who lives in Junction City, Kansas, drove off the side of a bridge and was drowned, you would undoubtedly dismiss the dream, except that before you put the strange dream out of your mind, you might wonder why on earth you would dream so unaccountably of Alfred. If, after having turned your thoughts to other matters, you were then to receive a long-distance telephone call to inform you that your cousin Alfred drove off the side of a bridge and was drowned, what would happen to your scientific attitude? Little shivers would run down your spine and your arms would prickle with chills. You would secretly wonder whether you possess un unusual sensitivity, carrying with it a superiority over others who were not clairvoyant. Your scientific objectivity would fly out of the window, or, at the very least, it would slowly flutter away. Your personal emotional experience would transcend intellectual conviction. In this situation, truth would certainly be dull, and fiction fascinating. You would surely mention your dream and its counterpart to your friends, most of whom would vicariously experience your mysterious thrill. No table of random numbers, no set of dice, no computer could compete with the excitement of your remarkable supposed intuition. The eerie stories of dreams which coincide with actual events perpetuate the feeling that dreams are more than products of the dreamer's imagination.

Once, in a seminar of twenty-eight insomniacs, we asked how many in the group believed that dreams were predictive. Two of the twenty-eight raised their hands in an unequivocal affirmative response. Two more hesitated, started to raise their hands, but then thought better of their tentative gesture and lowered their hands quickly. We also noticed uncertain expressions on two other faces. Twenty-two remaining members of the group were firm in their negative responses—dreams are not predictive. We later questioned the four who had registered hesitation or doubt. One woman told us that the suggestion that anyone at all would believe in the predictive power of a dream seemed so foolish to her that she doubted that she had heard correctly. A young man said that he believed in dreams as a vehicle of extrasensory perception, ESP, but that he had been reluctant to register what he knew would be a minority opinion. The two vacillating hand-raisers answered in terms which were vague and equivocal. We interpreted their responses to mean that dreams left them with premonitions which possessed private credibility, but nevertheless they felt that they could not rationally ascribe predictive power to dreams. In other words, they did not believe that dreams predicted approaching events, but at the same time they did feel that dreams served as omens.

Upon careful consideration, their position is not as unreasonable as it may seem at first glance. Who has not awakened from a happy dream feeling cheerful and optimistic? By the same token, troublesome dreams leave an aftermath of depression sometimes accompanied by half-formed forebodings of misfortune. Insomnia turbula, consequently, disturbs not only sleep, but the waking hours which follow. Turbula influences mood and thereby taints the emotional tone of the morning after the dream. Our group of twenty-eight revealed an additional psychological factor. At least five of the group, close to twenty percent, indicated some kind of belief, even if only hesitant, in the external power of dreams. In terms of drawing any scientific conclusion, the test is inadequate, but it does indicate that the association of dreams with the supernatural probably plays a significant role in afflicting victims of troubled sleep.

More potent than the vestigial forebodings which follow nightmares is the responsibility generated by Freudian precepts, and succinctly summarized by Eric Fromm: "You are the author of your dreams." Freud took responsibility for the dream away from external forces and placed it squarely in the mind of the dreamer. The Freudian formulation has captured the imagination of poets and writers as well as scientists. Delmore Schwartz titled his 1938 collection of poetry *In Dreams Begin Responsibilities.* Almost imperceptibly, the ideas percolated down through the layers of society, so that now, people who have never read Freud often assume responsibility for the content of their dreams. With Freud began responsibility, and in its wake, guilt. We usually observed guilt in turbula cases. One young woman said to us, "Why do these terrible ideas come into my mind? Why do I think such awful thoughts?" We also observed fear which extended beyond the events of the dreams themselves. "What is happening to me? What is wrong with my mind?" were silent questions.

Within the Freudian framework, the dream results from a breakthrough of material which, repressed during the day, escapes through the weaker defenses of sleep. Freud traced the dream content to primitive sexual impulses and longings, to incestuous Oedipal fantasies repressed because they were forbidden. When *The Interpretation of Dreams* was written, the Victorian climate was severely critical of sexuality. Freud saw the individual's need to express the primary sex drive as a pervasive force subjected to constant restraint. In the present-day, permissive social environment, sexuality is assumed to require less repression and the dream nucleus is interpreted more broadly by analysts, who nevertheless still follow the general hypothesis of Freud that dreams represent the expression of repressed desires. Continuing the Freudian conception, although repression, our first line of defense, is weakened when we are asleep, a second defense squad stands at the ready during the night to disguise the taboo material, so that it emerges in the dream with its true identity masked. The dreamer's conscience is thereby shielded from recognition of the naked needs which lie beneath the dream. The masks supplied by the defense squad serve to preserve the dreamer's supposed Victorian gentility. The second Freudian line of defense utilizes for its dream work the operations of condensation, symbolization, displacement, and secondary elaboration. These processes, operating upon material which is, at the outset, rational and logical, account for the bizarre nature of the dream.

Condensation, according to Freud, telescopes a number of events or persons so that they appear to be one event or one person. If you search through characters in your recent dreams, you may find at least one who seems to be one person whom you know, has the appearance of someone else, and who behaves like yet a third. Freudians would explain this as condensation. You may recall an event in a dream which also fits this paradigm. A football game played in a gymnasium with the players dressed in swim suits would incorporate several activities into a single dream unit and would constitute condensation. Condensation may also operate to express a complex idea in terms of a single image. One woman who was absorbed in passage of the Equal Rights Amendment dreamed, while in analysis, of a tiny semitropical marine animal known as the sea horse. Mulling this over through several sessions of analysis, she recalled that the male of the sea horse species bears the young, and so she finally interpreted the little fish to be a condensed expression of her struggle for equality.

Symbolization refers to the process whereby one object represents another. In Freudian terms, a dove represents peace. All long, pointed objects symbolize the penis; groups of three objects signify the male genitalia; an enclosed space such as a box portrays the womb; water depicts birth; and steps connote sexual intercourse. While these are universal symbols, Freudians caution that they are not to be used rigidly, as one uses ingredients in a recipe. Thus, it is possible for an umbrella to portray nothing more than an umbrella. However, the process of symbolization may substitute the umbrella for the original object in the mind of the dreamer. Symbolization may also take a slightly different form. We knew a man who, when he entered psychoanalysis, found himself dreaming nightly about American Indians. He was surprised. Although he had always been sympathetic to the plight of the American Indians, their cause had not engaged his attention or interest to any unusual extent. In his analytic sessions, he was unable, for several weeks, to discover meaningful associations to Indians. Finally, during one session, with the equivalent of "Eureka!" the symbolic meaning of Indian flashed into his mind. His last name was Rotemann, which, translated from German, means red man. The Indians in his dream symbolized himself. He had been dreaming of himself, he explained to his analyst, and in his dream he was disguised by a symbol, the Indian.

Displacement refers to the substitution of one person for another. This particular mechanism of dream interpretation was described by Anna Freud, the daughter of Sigmund, who observed that displacement is utilized during waking hours as well as in dreams. It is the most easily recognized of the day defenses, especially when others employ the technique to deflect to you their anger with someone else. In displacement, a second person becomes the target of an emotion which cannot, for one reason or another, be safely expressed toward the original object. If you have teen-age children, you may have noticed that they are prone to vent their school frustrations in angry outbursts at home. The wives of men experiencing financial reverses often suffer, as surrogates, scathing censure. One analytic patient, Louise, offered a graphic description of displacement within a nightmare.

Louise was an American, a woman who had always lived in moderate comfort but who, at the time of the dream, was inordinately depressed. Awake, she felt that her appearance was unattractive, although she was actually quite pretty. She felt that her intellectual capacity was at best only moderate, when in fact she was unusually intelligent. She thought of herself as inept and sharply deficient in social grace. She entered analysis because she did not like herself at all. Her dream, far removed from her own environment, was set in Nazi Germany. The dream opened in the sitting room of a house in the country. In the center of the room stood a crude, round table of unfinished pine. In the corner of the room, a lamp revealed the light of its electric bulb through a transparent shade. She later associated the lamp shade with Ilse Koch, the infamous Beast of Belsen, murderer of men, women, and babies. The room was still, no sound was heard, but it throbbed with danger. Louise stood rigidly in a corner of the room, sick with terror. A nightmare was about to unfold. The door, musty with the odor of damp wood, opened slowly. Observing the movement of the door, Louise drew back instantly, crouching behind the sofa. A hideously ugly woman entered the room. The woman was huge, five feet nine or ten, and almost two hundred pounds. She wore heavy boots and a loose, long, black skirt. Her face was bulbous, the skin mottled. She towered inside the room as she turned her head, searching. Behind the sofa, Louise, frail and helpless, trembled. The huge woman turned as if to leave, but then abruptly stopped. She was looking directly at Louise. Louise ran from behind the couch, hoping to escape by leaping through an open window at the other end of the room. The woman followed, lumbering heavily a few feet behind her. Louise ran with every ounce of her strength, straining for freedom, terror pounding in her head. The huge woman was gaining ground, and Louise could almost feel the fat fingers touch her back. In a moment, the woman would catch her and kill her. Louise awakened abruptly. The nightmare ended.

Because of her analytic orientation, Louise asked herself some questions. "Who is she? Do I know an ugly woman? Who is clumsy? Who is beastly? Who is tormenting me? Who is trying to kill me?" Only one name supplied the answer to all of these questions—Louise. Louise was the source of her own torment, she was her own assailant. In the dream, the process of displacement had substituted the Nazi sadist for Louise herself. Both of the characters in the dream represented the dreamer. Displacement substituted a brutal character for the dreamer's own conception of herself. This was Louise's Freudian evaluation of her nightmare. Within the Freudian postulation, displacement as a dream mechanism is employed by the superego, or conscience, in order to hide the true identity of the leading characters in the imaginary drama.

Secondary elaboration occurs after the dream has ended, during the dreamer's recall of the dream. Missing details are supplied, emphasis is shifted, and subtle changes in the fabric of the plot are embroidered. Secondary elaboration brings to mind the parlor game, wherein an involved story is whispered by one person to the next in turn until everyone in the room has heard in this manner an account of the facts. The final story, repeated aloud for all to hear, has changed drastically from the original version, often beyond recognition. This process may also be noted in relation to the ominous rumors which circulate in times of social unrest. Within the Freudian formulation, the dreamer follows the same procedure. After the dream, he employs secondary elaboration to alter its content, and thereby unconsciously masks the forbidden desires which threaten the moral code.

Freud observed that dreams are often sparked by events which occurred on the preceding day. Recent research has confirmed this observation, further noting that the first dream of the night tends to show a strong relationship to daytime experience, while later dreams during the same night shift away to other matters. Freud's term for the events of the day which appear in the dream is the *day residue.* The actual events in the dream, that is the plot or story line, comprise the manifest content. The term *manifest content* describes your dream's fascinating story, which you enthusiastically relate to your friend, and it describes as well the tedious narrative which your friend insipidly recounts when he describes his dream to you.

Buried beneath the manifest content, disguised and distorted by the dream work processes of condensation, symbolization, displacement, and secondary elaboration, lie the primitive desires which struggle for expression. This primary core is referred to as the *latent content.* Freudian analysis attempts to work from the manifest content down to the latent content, and thence to discover the neurotic disturbance of the patient undergoing analysis.

Most important for the illumination of the nightmare within this system is the guiding principle which states that always, at the heart of the dream, there is the wish. The dream, and the nightmare, are seen as an expression of a wish. The fright, the horror, the pounding heart, the frantic gasps for breath represent the dreamer's reaction to the evil wish and simultaneously constitute a disguise which substitutes fright as a protestation of innocence in the place of illicit desire.

Various alterations in Freud's basic interpretation of dreams have appeared. Most practicing therapists do not necessarily trace the wish to a sexual origin. More emphasis is placed upon current day-to-day conflicts which confront the patient. The day residue therefore assumes a more important role than the one originally assigned. Largely, however, the system remains the same, and the manifest content is reduced, via free association, to the latent content of the dream.

Before we analyze the Freudian system of dream interpretation, we wish to make it clear that we endorse and recommend psychotherapy in many instances. When troubled sleep is simply one of several manifestations of an emotional distress, psychotherapy is appropriate, and in some cases it is necessary. Any type of therapy which helps and comforts the patient and at the same time incurs no dangers is desirable. Our objections apply to the analytic mystique which substitutes one danger for another and which, like the dreams it purports to interpret, is impregnated with distortion. It is apparent that the Freudian interpretation of dreams utilizes evidence which proves no case at all. Given the dream processes wherein one person may represent himself, herself, or someone else of the same or opposite sex at any age (displacement), where an object may assume its own identity or may alternately substitute for another object (symbolization), where an event or person may depict a single or several entities (condensation), where the dreamer's own account of his dream is suspect (secondary elaboration), where accuracy is rare and distortion is rife, it is clear that any manifest content of any kind may be reduced to any latent content of any kind, depending only on the beliefs and the philosophy of the analyst. The Freudian system is so loose that, given one complicated dream and the patient's associations to that dream, five different analysts might well arrive at five different interpretations. We can go even further and say that five different analysts would be very unlikely to reach the same interpretation.

Challenges to the Freudian interpretive system have appeared in various quarters. A major objection is that the system is retrospective only—it does not predict. Accordingly, it cannot be employed before an event. An analyst cannot take dreams, interpret those dreams, and from that interpretation accurately conclude that Subject A, for example, having dreamed in a particular pattern, will now do something specific, or suffer a certain type of neurosis, or exhibit any given prevailing mood; nor can the analyst offer any other objectively verifiable forecast regarding the dreamer. The Freudian theory, by reason of its retrospective nature, precludes submission to a test of validity. It cannot be proven. After seventy-nine years, it remains unproven.

The disclosures of the EEG, first employed to measure the dreaming process in the 1950s, offer evidence to challenge the

Freudian postulation. The basic assumption, the foundation of Freud's structure, poses the proposition that the dream represents repressed material. Repression results from the moral strictures of society, which are superimposed upon the primary needs of the individual. Freud reflected the moral climate of his own Victorian world. One could conceivably modify the locus of repression to the standards of any human society, from that of Sodom to the Shakers of New England, for whom all sex was prohibited. But even granting wide latitude, how can the dreams of lower animals, disclosed by use of the EEG, be explained within the Freudian system? Among the animals which exhibit dream sleep are macaque monkeys, chimpanzees, dogs, goats, sheep, rats, mice, and opossum. The opossum, which is a member of the marsupial family and carries its young in a pouch, dreams for fifty percent of the time spent in sleep. This finding is remarkable, in that the brain structure of the opossum shows it to be even less developed than the other animals tested. According to the Freudian interpretation, the opossum, by virtue of its dreams, would presumably be subject to repression, as would the other lower animals. What conceivable moral code is enforced by societies of mice, rats, goats, or opossums?

At the human level, questions arise from the results of EEG tests upon neonatal infants. Newborn babies show dream sleep for as much as eighty percent of their sleep time. They dream before society has had an opportunity to impose any moral restrictions at all. One wonders what the dreams of a newborn infant could mirror. Inasmuch as adult dreams are based upon adult experiences, infant dreams must similarly be based upon infant experiences. Patterns of light and shadow comprise the visual world of the infant, and so in all probability the infant's dream world reflects these same lights and shadows. But repression? No.

One experimenter who worked with cats as subjects produced the rapid eye movement of dreams, the familiar REM, by stimulating a section deep within the cat's lower brain, the brain stem. He speculated that dreams are provoked by automatic activity in the lower brain stem, where firings activate, in turn, the higher brain activity of dreams. This speculation, while lacking the imaginative drama which we find so interesting, nevertheless accounts for the dream sleep of animals and infants, as well as the dream sleep of adult humans. Its validity remains to be proven, but in any event it is more acceptable than the Freudian thesis which, unable to account for human dreams which occur in the absence of repression, is further negated by the evidence that repression-free organisms also dream.

Still another criticism has been leveled against the assumption that dreams represent repressed material. If dreams represent repressed material, it follows that wide variations in dream quantity should be observed between separate individuals, and also within the same individual at different times, depending upon the changing reservoir of repressed material. Analysis should reveal a relationship between quantity of repression and quantity of dream activity. Thus, an individual with many repressions should experience more dreams than someone with fewer repressions. This is not the case. Any variations which have been observed thus far lack significance. As a general finding, dream sleep occupies roughly twenty-five percent of sleep time for most people, regardless of level of repression. A student troubled by this challenge to the assumption might well ask if the balance of the system could nevertheless stand intact. Our answer is no. The laws of science do not permit violation of a basic premise. Science, contrary to general belief, is not a body of knowledge; the elements of science do not consist of facts. Science is related to mathematics. It is comprised of a body of laws. These laws constitute the tools by which evidence, and deductions and inductions from evidence, are subjected to examination. To permit an infringement of a basic premise, while accepting conclusions founded on that premise, would be comparable to the practice of a building inspector issuing a certificate of occupancy for a house constructed on a crumbling foundation.

The Freudian system, resting on a crumbling foundation, nevertheless offers a number of attractions. It is a tantalizing, magnetic conception, which contains elements of apparent truth. It has permeated the thought of the Western world so that almost no person escapes its impact. Perhaps it is a philosophy, perhaps an art. It is a model, an ethic; above all, it is a gothic tale. Unfortunately, it does not meet the criteria of science.

Some research specialists have suggested that dreams may result from spontaneous neural discharge in the lower brain stem. The work of Wilder Penfield and his associates at McGill University in Canada sheds some light on a possible mechanism of dream production. Penfield, a neuro-surgeon, is renowned for his skill in brain surgery. For many years, patients from all parts of the world traveled to Canada to place themselves in his care. Brain surgery differs from other surgery in that the brain itself, once uncovered, registers no pain when it is cut or probed. In this respect, the brain is like the fingernail, except that it is a soft mass of tissue. You may have seen animal brains in the showcase of a butcher shop. The human brain is similar in appearance, a gray, half-globe covered by wrinkled serpentine convolutions called the cortex. During brain surgery, once the scalp has been placed aside in a flap for later restoration, and the skull drilled open to reveal the brain inside, the patient may then be brought back to consciousness to lend assistance to the surgery by a verbal report of his or her reactions.

This is the technique which Penfield employed. Before actual surgery was initiated, the surgeon, using a mild electrical current which simulated synaptic transmission, touched various sections of the cortex and asked the patient to describe the result of this cortical excitation. Through the use of this technique on many different patients, Penfield was able to draw a map of the cortex indicating the precise cortical area related to particular parts of the body. Stimulation of the top of the brain, the section which lies on either side of the line described by hair parted in the center, produced twitches in the hands, fingers, face, mouth, legs, or feet, depending upon the specific minute location of contact. Other adjacent areas produced sensations rather than actual twitches. Stimulation of the lower rear portion of the brain, the back of the head above the neck, resulted in flashes of light, indicating that the area was involved in vision. Stimulation of the temporal lobes, the portion of the brain which lies under the temples, led to a surprising result. At a touch in the temporal lobe area, the patient would experience the visual image, sometimes accompanied by the sound and the emotion, of a past experience. A memory was replayed as if a motion picture projectionist were running part of an old film. Sometimes the memory was clear and accurate. Sometimes it was vague, as in a déjà vu experience. And sometimes the memory was distorted—as in a dream.

Penfield performed his brain surgery in a surgical theatre at McGill in Canada, with the stage enclosed in glass. The patient, surrounded by Penfield and his medical team, lay upon the operating table. Apparatus blinked and bubbled; various meters flashed readings, which were checked every few seconds by a technician. Visiting physicians, medical students, psychologists, all crowded the raised gallery, peering through the glass at the drama below. Each quick, light touch of the electric needle was followed first by a long pause, and then by the voice of the patient, speaking in a matter-of-fact tone, and describing a fragment of an evoked memory.

One patient responded, after the stimulation, "There was a piano over there and someone playing. I could hear the song, you know." Then, after an additional touch of the needle, "Someone speaking to another and he mentioned a name but I could not understand it. . . . *It was like a dream.*" (Authors' italics.) After further electrical actuation the same patient went on, "Yes, Oh Marie, Oh Marie. Someone is singing it." And again, still the same patient, now prodded at a separate spot in the same general area. "Something brings back a memory. I can see Seven-Up Bottling Company—Harrison Bakery." The initial several stimuli evoked auditory impressions, while the last elicited the visual image of illuminated advertisements familiar to residents of Montreal.

A second subject, a woman, heard an orchestra playing a popular tune and was able when requested to hum along with the orchestra. Each time the needle was removed from the cortical area in her brain, without her knowledge of the removal, she reported that the music had stopped. When the needle was then reapplied, the orchestra began playing all over again as it did originally, at the very same point in the very same song. The patient heard the imagined music so clearly that she believed that a phonograph was playing in the operating room.

One young boy was able to hear the same telephone conversation which he had heard just before he left his home for the hospital. Another patient laughed with delighted surprise because, fully aware that he lay on an operating table in Canada, he discovered himself listening to a conversation of his friends in South Africa. Not all patients reported a memory experience. Some described distorted sights and sounds. Emotions were also evoked, yielding sensations of loneliness, fear, dread, and even panic.

In his article in *Science* ("The Interpretive Cortex," June 1959), Penfield also described a case which is particularly relevant to the study of dreams. With reference to this case, it is helpful to understand that epileptic attacks are occasioned by spontaneous electrical activity in the brain.

"In 1936, a girl of 16 (J.V.) was admitted to the Montreal Neurological Institute complaining of epileptic attacks, each of which was ushered in by the same hallucination. It was a little dream, she said, in which an experience from early childhood was reenacted, always the same train of events. She would then cry out with fear and run to her mother. Occasionally this was followed by a major convulsive seizure.

"At operation, under local anesthesia, we tried to set off the dream by a gentle stimulus in the right temporal lobe. The attempt was successful. The dream was produced by the electrode. Stimulation at other points on the temporal cortex produced sudden fear without the dream. At still other points, stimulation caused her to say that she saw 'someone coming toward me.' At another point, stimulation caused her to say she heard the voices of her mother and her brothers."

Penfield's work with cortical stimulation suggests that we maintain a library of memories, memories which are accessible either as replicas of experience or in distorted form, and which may be evoked by simply activating a critical neuron, by touching the correct button. The speculation that this process underlies our dreams remains a conjecture. As a model, it might well function in the partially random, automatic manner proposed by some physiologists. Spontaneous neural activity seems to originate in the lower brain and can account for animal as well as human dreams. These spontaneous impulses, traversing the length of the ascending neurons, would jump across the synaptic gap to spark the next higher level of neurons, setting off a random pattern of discharges, and with them the impressions and emotions we know as dreams. Such a supposition presents the possibility that the dream mechanism lies completely outside of the dreamer's responsibility, so that the dream expresses no wish, no impulse, no unconscious thought, but instead merely repeats a combination of impressions stored away through the history of the individual. No one knows the mechanism which vitalizes a dream. It would be futile to advise you to eliminate your horror after a nightmare. The emotion is part and parcel of the nightmare. The aftermath, however, the self-doubt which appears on the following day, need not occur.

If you are a victim of nightmares, you are in a position to halt them. We all possess substantially greater control of our behavior than we realize. We are accustomed to regard ourselves almost as leaves in the wind, subject to the whim of every passing breeze. Intelligent people often say that they cannot perform various simple chores. They cannot learn mathematics. They cannot bake cakes. The knack of planting flowers escapes them: "I don't have a green thumb." They are lost when they try to read road maps. Balancing checkbooks confuses them hopelessly. They create havoc when following mechanical directions. They are unable to sew a hem. Nonsense. Normally intelligent people can face all of these day-to-day problems successfully. Perhaps they do not wish to perform certain tasks, but if they undertook to master these and other skills, they could do so. People are also fond of claiming that they lose their tempers, that they are disorganized, that they are ruled by particular fears. These handicaps render them helpless, a condition which relieves them of many of the pressures we face in our daily lives. The claims of incapacity fill a need, but at the same time they mask our full range of powers, and they prevent us from resisting exploitation by forces within our system. The nightmare is one of these forces, and it can be resisted.

You must now organize a number of skills which you already possess so that you will awaken yourself as soon as a nightmare begins. The skills you require are, first, the ability to awaken at a signal, and second, the ability to alert yourself to the nightmare prologue, that portion of the dream which sets the stage for the frightening climax. The ability to awaken at a signal is widely acknowledged. The father of a teen-age son who borrows the family car will assure you that he always hears his son return home at night. The case of the mother who awakens at her baby's whimper is universally appreciated. Any selected sound may serve as the signal. In one study of awakening to a signal, the subjects slept in soundproof rooms which contained loud-speakers. All conditions were carefully controlled. Before going to sleep, the subjects were each assigned a specific taped sound, such as bagpipes, a telephone, a door bell, animal howls, Chinese gongs, or an airplane, and each subject was instructed to go to sleep and to awaken only on hearing his or her assigned sound. All of them went to sleep, and all of the taped sounds were played while they were sleeping. The subjects were able to accomplish the critical differentiation—to awaken only for a specific sound, and to sleep through all the others. You can make the same distinction with regard to the beginning of a nightmare.

Strange as it may seem, you are aware that you are dreaming when you dream. It seems that only part of you sleeps, while the other part steps aside to observe the process. In more than a dozen laboratories, experimental subjects have demonstrated their ability to transmit a signal to show that a dream has commenced. During these studies, EEG monitors verified that the signals occurred during dreams. In these experiments, the subjects usually moved a finger to indicate the onset of a dream. At Rush-Presbyterian-St. Luke's Medical Center in Chicago, patients in the sleep laboratory press a microswitch taped to the palm of the hand to signal that a dream has started, but not just any dream. They press the switch only for a particular kind of dream, only for a nightmare. In a similar procedure, you are going to awaken as soon as a dream assumes the unpleasant nightmare tone. You are going to circumvent nightmares by awakening before they swell to frightening intensity. You are now going to assume control of your sleep and bar the door to nightmares.

Prescripts and Proscripts for Insomnia Turbula

If your turbula is reactive in response to a life situation, you are passing through a period which is part of the healing process. Grief is natural; without grief, recovery cannot begin. Poor sleep is your expression of sadness. You may find it difficult to believe that the worst of your despair will diminish, but it will. You must try to soothe yourself as a good mother would soothe you. You should not, however, during a period of reactive insomnia turbula, comfort yourself with measures that convert a transient situation into a habit. The following prescripts and proscripts are particularly applicable to reactive turbula, but they may be used advantageously in cases of spontaneous turbula as well.

• Do not tranquilize yourself by lying in bed while you read, eat, drink, telephone, or watch television programs.

• If you awaken during the night, do not eat, and do not drink anything except water. Make absolutely certain you avoid alcohol at this time. Even when you are out of bed, do not read interesting material, do not watch television programs, and do not engage in any other activity which will reward awakening during the night.

• Do not take sleep medication for more than ten consecutive days, and *never, never* increase the prescribed dosage. This pro-script is of prime importance.

• If for any reason connected with your grief or shock you find it absolutely necessary to nap during the day, go to bed later than your accustomed time that night, or rise earlier the following morning.

• Engage in as much physical exercise as possible. A tired body will induce deep Stage 3 and Stage 4 sleep and thus counter-balance the dreams which disturb you. Try to remember that every day is a healing day. In time, as the healing process does its work, your turbula will pass away.

Nightmares

The self-alert system presented below can end the tyranny of troubled dreams. It will also deliver a bonus to you. It will demonstrate to you that you hold more power over yourself than you ever suspected. You will then be ready to use this same power in areas of your life which are far removed from sleep. Use it well.

A troubled dream, and particularly a nightmare, can be short-circuited before it can generate distress. The following measures may be used whether your turbula is reactive or spontaneous.

• You must alert yourself to awaken from sleep as soon as a nightmare begins. This decision, in and of itself, with no further instruction, is usually all that is required to abort the nightmare.

• As an additional aid, in order to furnish you with a sense of security, you may also bring into sharp focus the particular warning signals which presage your nightmares. These signals will mark the nightmare prologue for you just as arrows mark critical junctions on a highway. Answer the following questions:

1. Are your nightmares placed in a typical setting, a room, a place, a time? If so, what is the setting? Describe it to yourself. Decide now to awaken whenever you see this same stage set in a dream.

2. Does any one person, or a particular type of person, or do a number of specific persons appear in your nightmares? What are the distinguishing characteristics of this person or persons? Mark them well and arouse yourself each time you meet such person or persons in your dream.

3. Are any special sounds heard in your dreams—music, thunder, voices? Or do you perhaps notice a pervading silence? Remember to awaken each time you hear such sound, or are aware of such silence.

4. Do your nightmares begin with a particular emotion which you always experience at the onset of a dream? Frequently, the events of a nightmare are preceded by a feeling of fright, dread, or by a premonition of danger. In Louise's nightmare, recounted in this chapter, the dream opened in an empty room. Louise described her dream with the words, "The room was still, but it throbbed with danger." Think for a few minutes right now and make an attempt to describe your own typical nightmare emotion. Uneasiness, fright, terror, dread? The emotion need not be strong or even negative. One turbula victim realized that her nightmares followed an interlude in which she laughed with amusement. If you discover a typical emotional portent, use it as a marker to awaken yourself whenever you encounter in your dream this augury of fear.

5. Can you think of any other specific characteristics which earmark your nightmares? Examine these characteristics carefully, so that you will be certain to recognize them when they appear in your dreams.

6. Do your nightmares follow particular waking activities? A young writer often experienced nightmares after he attended a creative writing seminar. If your nightmares typically follow an activity which you cannot avoid, make sure to reaffirm your decision to awaken to portents of the

nightmare on the nights when you are especially vulnerable.

• When you awaken from your aborted nightmare, you must take precautions not to fall back to sleep immediately and thus risk continuation of the same dream. Therefore, for the first two weeks, follow this procedure:

1. Leave your bed.

2. Sit in a chair, preferably in another room. Remain in the chair for five minutes.

3. During these five minutes, stroke your right forearm with the fingertips of your left hand for approximately thirty seconds. This exercise is designed to interfere with, and thus terminate, the pattern of neural excitation which accompanied the dream. After five minutes, you may return to your bed.

You will experience no difficulty in following the prescript to awaken at the beginning of a nightmare. But initially you will probably also eliminate part or all of your deep sleep. For the first weeks, the quality of your sleep will seem to be lighter than before. As you gain confidence in your ability to awaken at will, you will be able to abandon yourself to deeper sleep, while still maintaining vigilance. At this point, you may give up the practice of leaving your bed after awakening to the nightmare signal.

One of our participants using this self-alert system slept lightly and at times uneasily, as predicted, but never needed to actually awaken at all. The nightmares vanished. They were replaced, occasionally, by uneasy dreams, which, mild by any standard, were innocuous in comparison with the nightmares. Then, over a long period, even the troubled dreams faded in intensity. Repetitive nightmares were compared by one research specialist, Dr. Ismet Karacan, to "a phonograph needle stuck in a single groove on a record." Your self-alert system allows you to lift the needle so that it moves ahead, away from the groove of the nightmare, and then proceeds to play out your dreams in normal fashion.

In summary:
• Do not eat, drink, telephone, watch television, etc., in bed.

- Do not eat or drink anything except water during the night. Alcohol must be scrupulously avoided.
- Do not take prescribed sleep medication for more than ten consecutive days.
- Never increase the prescribed dosage of a drug.
- If you occasionally nap during the day, go to bed later than usual that night.
- Tire yourself with physical activity.
- Study the prologues to your nightmares or unpleasant dreams.
- Alert yourself to awaken as soon as a bad dream or nightmare begins.
- For the first two weeks of your program, when you awaken from an aborted nightmare, leave your bed. Sit in a chair for five minutes. During these five minutes, briefly stroke your right forearm with the fingertips of your left hand.
- After the initial two-week period, when you awaken from an aborted nightmare, you may remain in bed, but spend a few minutes awake stroking your forearm before you allow yourself to sink back into sleep.

CHAPTER 7

Fear of Death

The telephone call had reached Alice at her office in New York. She accepted the news calmly, returning to the conference table and completing the business of the meeting, devoting her full attention to the matter under discussion. Then she explained briefly and hurried home. There, although still calm, she found herself unable to make the simple preparations for the flight to Florida. She could not organize herself sufficiently to pack a bag or to travel to the airport. She delayed until the following morning, walking aimlessly back and forth, wandering to the bathroom for toothpaste and forgetting her objective when she reached the medicine cabinet, packing a skirt, then substituting a dress instead.

She rode a taxi directly from the airport to St. Francis Hospital. Her mother's eyes filled with tears. "I didn't know if you would come," her mother murmured. For the first week, visiting was permitted for ten minutes in each hour, from five minutes to the hour until five minutes after. Alice spent the balance of the time in the waiting room, or walking on the sun-flooded streets. The following Monday she arrived at the hospital to find her mother transferred from the intensive care unit to her own room, and so she was now free to visit at any time. She brought cosmetics and new nightgowns and helped her mother to dress.

She combed her mother's hair awkwardly. Alice was unaccustomed to combing someone else's hair—her own child was a boy and he was grown now. Running the comb through her mother's hair, she felt for the first time a strange transfer of roles, a maternal feeling for her mother.

It seemed to Alice that she had spent most of her life, almost all of her life, as a visitor to her mother in a hospital room. It was an odd illusion, for her mother had been hospitalized on only three previous occasions, and yet the hospital surroundings struck her now with an impact that recalled to memory the same antiseptic odor, the same hushed sounds, the same mysterious routines of the other three hospitals. Each of her separate hospital impressions merged in this instant to form in their totality an image large enough to blot out the rest of her life.

Her mother had been hospitalized once in childbirth when Alice was sixteen, once for a mastoid infection during the Second World War, and a third time for phlebitis. And now this fourth time for a mild heart attack. Each time Alice dutifully sat at the bedside all day, every day, for the entire length of the hospital stay. On this occasion her mother was in good spirits and seemed in good health, except for a general debility. Alice had not anticipated her mother's lighthearted mood. She was smiling as she rested her head against the high back of the wing chair, and this surprised Alice, for her mother was usually subdued, even depressed. Yet now, after a heart attack at seventy, sitting in a chair for the first time after the attack, she hummed along with the radio, waving her hand to the rhythm of the music. Like a little girl, Alice thought with a surge of tenderness. Watching her mother move her hand languidly in time to the music, she experienced again the protective feeling of a parent for a child who is weak.

Her mother closed her eyes, then opened them. "I'm so tired," she sighed. "I don't know why I'm so tired." Alice helped her back into the bed, and then sat in a chair near the window. Outside, the top of a ragged palm tree reached almost as high as the windowsill. A warm patch of sunlight fell on her face. Sitting in the chair, Alice dozed lightly. She awakened only moments later. Her mother was lying on her back, her eyes closed. A rasping sound came from her throat. Chilled, Alice leaped from her chair and stared. Her mother was dead.

All of the members of the family joined her in Florida for the funeral. She stayed for two weeks to close her mother's apartment. Except for flashes of devastating grief, Alice remained calm and self-possessed. While cleaning, she found a vial marked Placidyl (sleep medication) in the medicine cabinet, and when she could not sleep, she took a capsule. She was surprised when her mother's neighbor remarked that she looked worn out. She saw no difference in herself.

On her first night back in her own home, Alice awakened suddenly. She felt alert and wide awake. The digital clock read 4:32. In the other bed, her husband was asleep. An outline of cartons darkened the wall beneath the window. Alice and her husband had moved into the new apartment only a month earlier, two weeks before her mother's death. These few cartons were still unpacked. In the dark, Alice could feel her own heartbeat, strong and steady. She stepped out of bed and tiptoed into the living room. Through the large window, high above Queens, she could see the outlines, in lights, of the city beyond, the green sparkling loops of the smaller bridges, then the majestic Triboro scrawled into longer, deeper waves of lights, the inverted spike of the Empire State Building, and all the way to the left, the blinking red lights around the top of the twin towers of the World Trade Center. The view, even at this hour with most of the city darkened, was spectacular. She felt as if it all belonged to her, as if she were a millionaire or a motion picture star. Only a few weeks earlier, her mother had eagerly promised to visit in the spring. Now she would never visit. Never. Alice began to cry. No more telephone calls. Never. No more letters in the mailbox. Never again. No more birthday cards. No more gifts. No more affectionate names. No more little pats. No more smiles of pride. She remembered how she had felt when she was a child. She wanted her mother. At five o'clock in the morning, she returned to bed exhausted.

A few nights later, she awakened again with a start. She felt a curious sensation of having been energized, stimulated. The room was dark. She lit her bedside lamp. It was 4:49. She slipped out of bed quietly. In the living room, a stack of blank thank-you notes lay alongside the guest list from the funeral parlor. She picked up the list and started to address each of the envelopes, locating the addresses in her mother's telephone book or in her own. So many names. And yet her mother had been lonely. So many envelopes, and yet her mother had been timid, always so eager to be accepted by each new person she met. Alice ached with the memory of her mother's lonely pain. When her fingers felt numb, she stopped addressing the envelopes, and although it was still early and her eyes burned with lack of sleep, she dressed for the office.

Awakening in the middle of the night several times each week, she filled the extra hours with the tasks which follow death. When all of the thank-you notes were mailed, all of the letters written, all of the bills paid, all of the forms completed, all of the agencies notified, all of the possessions distributed, Alice still found herself opening her eyes suddenly after only four or five hours of sleep. She realized that she had developed insomnia.

When we questioned insomniacs, we found that a surprisingly large number of problems were precipitated by or associated with a vivid experience with death. We reached the inescapable conclusion that insomnia is often rooted in a fear of death. One participant, Rachel, looked up while filling out a questionnaire and asked, "How do you spell synonymous?" On the questionnaire Rachel wrote, "To me sleep is synonymous with death." Rachel's insight was rare. Many people refer casually to a death-related experience in connection with the onset of insomnia, but they usually do not link the two events. A few women recognized that they feared death in sleep, but no men ever volunteered an admission of fear.

It is not strange that men deny an acquaintanceship with fear. In our society, fear, a natural, self-protective emotion, is considered unseemly in females and unmanly in males. This attitude is reflected even by children in interview situations unrelated to sleep. The routine question "What frightens you?" invariably elicits the answer "Nothing" from boys, and from girls as well with slightly less frequency. We have seen battered children who have suffered abuse. We have seen six-year-olds who flinch at the approach of a stranger. We have seen children who have been passed from one foster home to another as if they were inanimate objects. We have seen children who hear terrible voices speaking to them in the dead of night. The answer that even these children give is "Nothing." We have also seen children of limited intellectual ability. They do not learn as well as other children. Their answer nevertheless is the same: "Nothing." All of these children will tell you exactly what makes them happy, or angry, or sad, but they all deny fear. Society teaches its lesson well. Fear is prohibited, banned, proscribed—taboo. Unfortunately, fear is not governed by the laws of society. Fear emerges according to another set of dictates, sometimes brazenly, often in disguise, and ocassionally the disguise is insomnia.

If children learn early in life to deny or to suppress their fears, is it any wonder that adults proceed one step further, repressing their fear, refusing to recognize the emotion even in the secret places of their own awareness?

We are not suggesting that every victim of insomnia is repressing the fear of death. We are suggesting that if your sleep problem bears a close association to death, either through chronology of onset, through your own free associations, or through any other connection, you must further explore the possibility that you are afraid to sleep.

Fear of sleep is fear of death. The visual similarity of sleep to death unquestionably creates a fusion of the two in the mind of an observer. This marriage of sleep to death is incorporated into early human thought. Sir James Frazier, in *The Golden Bough*, describes the pagan belief that sleep is a temporary form of death. According to primitive thought, death represents a permanent departure of the soul from the body, while sleep corresponds to a temporary absence of the soul. The conceptual kinship of sleep and death was personified in Greek, and then Roman, mythology. In ancient Greece, the twin brothers Hypnos and Thanatos were the gods of sleep and death, respectively. Similarly, the Roman god Somnus was the god of sleep, while his twin brother Mors reigned over death.

This conception, that sleep is the twin of death, has survived the pagans. It is so persuasive, and has become so much a part of us, that we find it repeated and emphasized by our poets through the ages. Aristophanes refers to death as "an eternal sleep." In Book XVI of *The Iliad*, Homer speaks of

Sleep and Death, two twins of wingèd race
Of matchless swiftness, but of silent pace.

Plutarch, in his *Consolation to Apollonius*, quotes Diogenes, who, on falling into a slumber shortly before his death, responded to his physician's question as to whether anything ailed him with the reply: "Nothing sir; only one brother anticipates another,— Sleep before Death." Shelley remarks "How wonderful is Death— Death and his brother Sleep," and Swinburne in his "Hymn to Proserpine" observes that "there is no God found stronger than death, and death is a sleep." The list is endless, recurring over and over again in our literature, that unerring reflector of our culture. They are twins. Sleep, the twin of death.

The similitude of these twins suggests that the distinction between them is only one of degree. The conception of death as a profound sleep, and conversely of sleep as a dilute form of death, carries terrifying implications. When sleep is seen as the outskirts of the valley of death, then an excursion into sleep threatens the possibility that the boundary of no return may be inadvertently crossed over.

Children are especially prey to a primitive fear of sleep:

Now I lay me down to sleep
I pray the Lord my soul to keep
If I should die before I wake
I pray the Lord my soul to take

One little girl we encountered read the four familiar lines in a storybook and memorized the prayer as a symbolic amulet to protect her during the night. Children seem to find this prayer comforting, perhaps because it first expresses their own anxiety and then undertakes to drive it away.

The common aspects of sleep and death are more striking to children and the uninformed than to sophisticated adults. The similarity is of course more apparent than real, and achieves its strongest impact before an individual's critical powers are sharpened by experience and by learning. Inasmuch as fear of sleep is not rooted in reason, it cannot be uprooted by reason. Nevertheless, an examination of the similarities and differences is instructive. Sleep appears to be a slowdown of life processes, a sort of way station on the road to complete cessation of these processes. Actually sleep masks a wild acceleration of activity, the exact opposite of deceleration. Thus, during dream sleep, blood pressure spurts erratically. Heart rate increases. Both depth and rate of breathing fluctuate. The nervous system revs up like a racing car before the Indianapolis 500. Even during non-dream sleep, breathing deepens, digestion proceeds, and the hormones ACTH and cortisol are secreted—the very antithesis of a slowdown of life processes. Thus, notwithstanding the surface similarities, sleep and death are diametrically at odds with each other.

To many people, even more alarming than the presumed slowdown during sleep is the loss of contact with external events. Both sleep and death issue from a surrender of awareness of the outside world. Some people are truly intimidated by any separation from the sights, sounds, odor, and touch of their immediate environment. It is, of course, useless to inform them that they maintain contact during sleep. If you doubt the durability of your contact with your environment during sleep, ask yourself these questions. Do you doubt that a mother can awaken from a deep sleep at the whimper of her baby? Do you doubt that a nodding sentry can awaken at the snap of a twig? Do you doubt that most people can, if they choose, awaken at any specific time determined before they go to sleep?

The phenomena of the mother, the sentry, and the internal alarm clock are well established. The minute brain structure which enables one to awaken to a signal has been located and its function carefully studied. The structure, a network of cells and fibers, lies in the brain stem, that central portion of the brain which rises from the spinal cord to the globe of the two brain hemispheres. The network is known as the reticular activating system, and is referred to as the RAS. It transmits incoming messages to the brain surface, and it also receives information from higher regions of the brain, so that it operates as a signal station with incoming and outgoing messages passing through to reach their final destination. In order to relay only certain signals which are meaningful to you, the RAS must receive and evaluate each and every sound which falls upon your ears during the night. All the irrelevant sounds must then be discarded, while the few meaningful sounds are retained and telegraphed to the next higher brain station. Incidentally, it should be noted that, even without these special significant signals, in the normal course of events it is the RAS which performs the task of awakening you each morning.

The awakening of both the mother and the sentry result from the RAS transmitting the selected meaningful sound signals. If you have ever remained awake through the night, you have noticed that each hour brings its own distinctive sounds. The loveliest of these sounds are the bird songs at dawn. Even in cities, the summer birds sing at five o'clock in the morning, while the city traffic sounds ebb and flow according to the hour. The suburbs and the country also transmit their own distinctive aural punctuations throughout the night. The RAS is thought to employ its own computerized program to process sound clues as well as other internal clues to arrive at an estimation of the time.

Two of the internal clues in your body cycle are temperature, which starts to climb from its nadir in the early hours of the morning, and volume of urine, which accelerates its expansion in your bladder at the same time. In the past, whenever by chance you were awake at five or six in the morning, the sensations of temperature and bladder pressure registered in the recesses of your memory along with the time. Now, when you tell your RAS, before you go to sleep, to awaken you at a given time, it takes notice of these two indexes, as well as others, and then it sends a message to a higher station in your brain: "Hey, it's getting to be six o'clock, wake up!" This, then, is the hypothesized mechanism involved in the operation of the internal alarm clock. Of course, individuals will vary in the accuracy of their time estimation. Impulsive, tense people often find that they are jumping the gun—awakening prematurely several times during the night. For many people, however, the self-signal is amazingly accurate, attesting to the remarkable vigilance of the RAS as it maintains its persistent contact with the outside world throughout the sleep period. In any event, it is clear that we all remain in constant touch with our environment when we are sleeping, and it is this vigilant contact which takes us back to another of the vital distinctions between sleep and death: contact continuing throughout the entire period of sleep.

Those who are apprehensive about the apparent loss of contact during sleep should be reassured by this evidence of the activity of both the brain and the body during sleep. But of course they are almost never reassured. The explanations, however reasonable, do not alleviate fear because fear is rarely amenable to reason. So strong is the continuing need to retain contact that many surgical patients refuse a general anesthetic, preferring instead to monitor even the most menacing of operating room procedures. These patients cannot tolerate loss of consciousness. They feel that they must remain on guard to repel death's assault.

Melinda, a member of one of our groups, once actually did repel an assault of death. She succeeded in keeping death away from her child. She was deeply thankful, but now, at twenty-nine, Melinda could not sleep through the night. She was a young suburban mother, tall, and attractively bony in a modish way. Her hands were slim with long, red fingernails. Her clothes were in the current, exaggeratedly casual fashion. Her days were spent driving her young daughters back and forth to their preschool activities, attending to household chores, or shopping. She occupied herself with community affairs, participating with relish in the activities of affluent suburbia. Her insomnia was complicated by destructive sleep-related habits and by the lavish attentions of her adoring father-in-law, whose concern with Melinda's insomnia was almost equal to her own.

Melinda's two daughters, five and four, formed the focus of her life. When the second infant was five months old, Melinda developed an uncomfortable chest cold, and, in an effort to nurse it away, she remained in the house for several days. One afternoon, feeling slightly feverish, she lay down for a nap on a cot in the infant's room. When she awakened, the baby was cooing in the crib. Melinda lay on the cot for a few moments. Then she rose, wearily, and as she left the room she glanced at the baby, now suddenly still. It seemed to Melinda that the child's face had turned slightly blue. She did not seem to be breathing. Frantically, Melinda snatched the baby from the crib, slapping her hand against the infant's back in a frenzied effort to revive her, and then placed her open mouth to the mouth of the baby and breathed fast and hard, attempting a desperate approximation of mouth-to-mouth resuscitation. In less than a minute, the baby drew a sharp breath and began to cry, feebly. Melinda cried too. She sat at the edge of the cot, the infant hugged to her chest, and she rocked back and forth, sobbing aloud. The child recovered completely.

For the next few weeks, Melinda awakened several times each night to look at her infant. After several months, assured by her pediatrician that all danger of crib death had passed, Melinda was nevertheless still waking during the night. Once awake, she could not fall back to sleep. Somehow, she had condemned herself to perpetual vigilance. In the years which followed, Melinda continued to awaken during the night and to remain awake for extended periods. Her anxiety about her children had abated, and yet she awakened regularly each night. When her youngest girl reached the age of three, Melinda and her husband, leaving the two children in the care of their grandparents, flew to Spain on vacation. In Spain, with an ocean between Melinda and her children, she found herself still unable to sleep, and remained utterly baffled, by her apparently preconscious insistence upon worrying about her two little girls.

The truth of the matter was that Melinda had long overcome her anxieties about the children. In the months which followed the near tragedy, the locus of Melinda's fear had shifted. With complete lack of awareness, and generalizing from the encounter with her infant, Melinda was suffering a fear of the possibility of her own death during sleep, and it was this fear for herself, not for her children, which was now producing her insomnia. Melinda, like Alice, had suffered a traumatic encounter with death. Because death, the near death of her child, was associated with sleep, her normal fear of death had spread to include fear of sleep. Melinda could not sleep simply because she was afraid to sleep. She required a method which would enable her to sever the association of sleep with death. The method of terminating that sleep-death association and establishing a new, pleasant associative background for sleep will be described in the prescripts and proscripts at the end of this chapter.

Still another feature common to both sleep and death involves the element of inaccessibility. The mild degree of inaccessibility in sleep is normally undisturbing, even to children. It acquires its horrifying implications only after exposure to a dead body. The bewildered child who sees death is faced with a threatening combination: a physical presence which, while within reach, is at the same time infinitely remote. In order to appreciate the terrifying threat of this combination, it must be examined in the context of the emotional and cognitive development of a child, of ourselves, for example, when we were children. In the early stages of development, babies do not understand that people and objects which are out of sight nevertheless still continue to exist. A feeding bottle may elicit vigorous kicks and coos, together with other evidence of excitement, and yet if the bottle is placed behind a pillow while the baby watches, no interest in the pillow follows. For the baby, the bottle has ceased to exist. When the mother leaves the room, the mother also ceases to exist. Then, slowly, in every baby, in every culture, in every part of the world, object constancy develops. The baby acquires an understanding that people and things which disappear also reappear. When an infant plays peek-a-boo, laughing delightedly when, having covered your face with your hands, you then remove your hands quickly, the baby is savoring this enchanting idea. It is only after object constancy has been fully grasped that the baby can learn to trust, and then to become a separate, independent individual.

All of us, in the course of our development, learn that the unseen may still exist, and upon this solid foundation we have learned to trust. Later, much later, confronted with death, we are faced with the obverse: that which we see may, at the same time, have actually ceased to exist. Object constancy is inherently delightful. Babies invariably laugh with enjoyment at the discovery. Conversely, object inconstancy seems to carry inherent horror; for just as trust is based upon object constancy, mistrust is based upon object inconstancy. And when we cannot trust, we cannot abandon ourselves to sleep.

Marion was unable to trust herself to sleep. She became dependent upon tranquilizers, which she used every night to help her to fall asleep. She attributed her poor, light sleep to heredity and to prevailing tension. It was quite true that she was tense, and it was also true that her mother had complained of inability to sleep for many years before her death. It required an illuminating incident, however, to acquaint Marion with the idea that a third factor was also operating to keep her awake.

Marion was a small, thin, active woman. She spoke quickly. She walked quickly. When she sat down, legs crossed, one foot bobbed nervously, or else, with both feet on the floor, she would drum her fingers lightly on the table. We never saw her in a relaxed position, and, by her own report, she was rarely able to unwind. Marion told us that, like her mother, she always slept poorly. There is a good chance that both of them enjoyed reasonably good sleep in terms of quality, but that their quantitative requirements were below the level of most people. In any case, Marion estimated that she slept no more than three hours a night. To make matters worse, in order to sleep for those meager three hours, she acquired the habit of using tranquilizers repeatedly, a number of pills each night. Before consulting us, she read alarming newspaper articles warning against the continued use of tranquilizers. Marion wanted to stop using the pills, but she needed a plan and support while breaking the habit.

We mapped out a gradual withdrawal schedule which we asked her to submit to her physician. As she followed that schedule, reducing the dosage weekly, she told us about herself. Married to a dentist, she was a principal in an elementary school in the New York City school system. Social changes in the schools during the seventies required a constant adjustment on her part. Marion was now fifty-eight years old. Years earlier, at the outset of her teaching career and for some time thereafter, pupils and parents alike treated her with enormous respect, even awe, but those attitudes were gradually changing, and in recent years she had had to learn to cope with parents who demanded their "rights," often with open hostility, and with children who addressed her either fondly as "Teach" or furiously with epithets that made her shudder. Almost every day brought a new problem, a novel situation, a unique challenge.

Marion was flexible, capable of adjusting to new situations, the youngest and brightest of eight children, and the favorite and pet of a large family. She was especially fond of her mother, who indulged her and took noticeable pride in her every achievement. Her mother had died at sixty of cancer, when Marion was twenty. Marion was vague as to precisely when her sleep problem began, but she indicated that in any event her insomnia was intensified after her mother's death, and many years later Marion began using the pills which her doctor prescribed.

Reduction of her sleep medication was now painful for Marion. During the day she suffered severe attacks of anxiety, trembling and perspiring without apparent cause. When she finally fell asleep at night, she would sink into a macabre nightmare from which she awakened abruptly. But she was determined to give up drugs, and gradually, as she followed the schedule strictly, the nightmares and the attacks of anxiety faded. One evening, Marion arrived at our office, sat down, and sighed.

"What happened?" we asked, although the answer was clear.

"I'm back," she answered. "The whole thing. Every pill. Every night. I can't help it. I just can't help it."

"Why?"

"We went to see a play with old friends. I wanted to leave after ten minutes, but I didn't want to spoil their evening. I didn't realize it would affect me so deeply."

"What was the name of the play?"

"The Shadow Box."

Although we had not seen the play, we had read the reviews. "So you stayed?" we asked.

"We stayed. Then we went out for a snack. I felt all right at first. But when we got home, I knew I wouldn't sleep. It was impossible."

"Were the others upset by the play?"

"They said it was gloomy. But it didn't seem to bother them."

"What about your husband?"

"He felt that it was interesting, a little bit depressing, but very interesting. I feel that I'll never sleep again," Marion added.

The play, well received by the critics, concerned a man dying of cancer.

"Exactly what about the play upset you?" we asked.

"It reminded me of my mother. She had cancer too." That was as far as Marion could go. The play upset her. It depressed her. It reminded her of her mother's lingering death. She was too distressed to sleep.

"Are you too upset to work?" we asked.

"No," she replied. "I feel better at work. Yesterday four teachers called in sick. I couldn't get four subs, and I had to rearrange classes and schedules for the entire day. I didn't have a spare minute to think."

"Are you able to take care of your home?" we continued.

"I don't do much at home," she explained. "I telephone my food orders and I send out the laundry."

"You can take care of those details without difficulty?"

"Yes," she said.

"And your social life?"

She looked at us blankly. The import of the question puzzled her. "We're driving to New England on Saturday to see the autumn leaves. We take the drive every year at this time with another couple."

We summarized. "You saw a play about death. You are able to do everything as usual, but you cannot sleep. Is that correct?"

"Yes," she agreed.

"Why can't you sleep?"

"I'm upset," she murmured. She could go no further.

Marion's mother died when Marion was twenty, and as she observed the lingering illness, aware, on a personal level, of death in its actual approach, Marion developed an intense fear of death. Because of the subliminal association of death and sleep, common to most of us, Marion's fear of death spread to its counterpart, the twin brother we mentioned earlier, sleep. Marion was now afraid to sleep, and that fear would surge or ebb, depending on external factors with which she came in contact. The play, with its emphasis on death, had abruptly reactivated her panic in all of its original strength, and consequently it reactivated and intensified her fear of sleep. Ultimately, Marion was able to conquer her drug habit, and her insomnia as well.

In this chapter, we have described several factors common to sleep and death. They are similar in appearance. They both seem to involve a slackening of vital processes. They both exclude conscious contact with the external world, and they both render the subject inaccessible. These shared attributes are not, however, responsible for fear-based insomnia. Fear of sleep is not based directly upon factors as rational or as irrational as the common attributes of sleep and death. The fear of death during sleep arises out of a purely automatic, universal, psychological phenomenon known as *generalization*. When a baby learns to identify a dog as "doggie," it will then say "doggie" to a cat or to a cow. Some babies chirp "da-da" to their fathers, and then to other men as well. The babies are generalizing from a specific object to a class of objects. As adults, we all generalize on both simple and complex levels. The specific: A woman awakens in a hotel at night startled and frightened by a rat scurrying across the room. The generalization: She develops a terror of mice, squirrels, and chipmunks, as well as rats. The specific: A man with a hoarse voice once cheated you. The generalization: You distrust men with hoarse, low, or gruff voices.

Statesmen and other important public figures are the beneficiaries of generalization. Astute politicians often take advantage of the phenomenon with cold calculation, as when they invariably agree to march in a parade, any parade, almost every parade. The specific: Mayor O'Leary marches in the Pulaski Day parade. The generalization: Mayor O'Leary is one of us. Similarly, prominent officials automatically acquire the dignity which accompanies the position which they occupy. On one clear winter evening, a number of New Yorkers stood witness to the process of generalization. The late President Kennedy, then newly elected, visited New York City. The visit had not been announced. It was late December. Park Avenue was crowded with automobiles and with shoppers returning to their homes. Suddenly, at this busy hour, southbound traffic stopped. A solitary policeman on a motorcycle rode slowly down the center of the lanes which lie to the west of the Park Avenue mall. Behind the motorcycle, nothing. Nothing at all for at least one suspenseful minute. All cross traffic was halted by policemen. Pedestrians paused to watch curiously. Expectations were stirred. Then a phalanx of motorcycle police in military formation, sirens screaming, appeared crawling along the avenue.

The expectations now intensified. Two black limousines, widely spaced but driving abreast, followed the policemen. They were filled with men in black hats, emphasizing the solemnity of the procession. Behind them, one single, polished, long, black, bubble-topped automobile rolled down the very center of the avenue. As it inched its way along the avenue, word passed from one spectator to another. "The President." "The President." And again. "The President." In the recognition which followed, the flush of excitement engendered by the sudden halt of traffic, the military formation, the screaming sirens, the intense solemnity of the procession, was transferred from the somber, impressive motorcade to the handsome leader in the regal limousine. In that moment, the man who had gained the intellectual support of many of the people on that street acquired, for almost everyone, supporters or not, an emotional overlay through a process of generalization. The excitement of the spectators generalized from the scene to the person.

The process of generalization may also mediate a transfer from one person to another, from one situation to another, and from one condition to another, as from death to sleep. Generalization is not a random occurrence. It always crosses a bridge. The bridge which connects sleep with death is the similarity, however superficial, of the two. The bridge is supported by constant, inescapable, explicit and implicit pairing of the two conditions. The literary references, the conversational allusions, the mythological kinship, the twinship, are all responsible for an associational bond, a link. It is this linkage which facilitates the transfer of fear of death to fear of sleep. It is this associational connection which was responsible for Alice's insomnia, for Melinda's insomnia, for Marion's insomnia, and which may be responsible for your insomnia as well.

In the final analysis, you and only you can decide whether or not you are fearful. If, at this point, you reject the suggestion that fear is your problem, your decision is probably correct. However, if you detect even a faint, lingering uncertainty within yourself, answer the questions which follow. They will help you to resolve your doubts.

Do you awaken with a start, feeling alert immediately? Many admittedly fearful people experience this type of awakening.

Are you at all afraid of the dark? If not, were you ever, even as a child, fearful of darkness? Did you ever prefer to sleep with a light in the room? Darkness is related to death by association. Fear of darkness suggests that fear is generalizing from darkness to sleep.

If you were offered a choice of anesthetics to be used during major surgery, would you choose a spinal anesthetic, which would merely deaden sensation, or would you choose general anesthesia, which would send you into a deep sleep? Fear of surgery, a process involving a sharp physical insult to the body, is most natural. Surely, the easiest method of diminishing this insult is by sleeping through it. The probabilities are strong that only a deeper fear will induce a rejection of general anesthesia. If you would prefer to remain awake during surgery, the odds are high that you are harboring an active fear of death, which, of course, may be easily transferred to a fear of sleep.

Does your sleep problem bear a chronological relationship to death; in other words, did your sleep difficulties begin shortly after an exposure to the death of someone you knew? If so, this constitutes, at the very least, circumstantial evidence that your insomnia may be related to a subconscious fear of death. Bear in mind that we refer to this only as circumstantial evidence—it is far from conclusive. If *b* follows *a* we certainly cannot conclude by that fact alone that *b* is caused by *a*. This line of reasoning would lead to the conclusion that thunder is caused by lightning. On the other hand, no detective worth his badge would disregard the presence of a stranger at the scene of a crime. Thus, if your problem appeared initially, or was subsequently intensifed following a death, the element of fear of death as a factor in your insomnia remains a strong possibility.

We wish that we could offer to those of you whose insomnia is related to fear, one quick, safe, surefire weapon which would enable you to demolish that fear immediately and permanently. We have no such weapon. Just as fear undermined your sleep surreptitiously, under cover of darkness, you must defend yourself in a series of minor skirmishes. If you should feel discouraged, keep in mind the lesson which recent history has so clearly demonstrated. In the end, the war is won in small battles, at secondary outposts, with hit-and-run guerrilla tactics, by unyielding determination.

Prescripts and Proscripts for Fear of Death

• In order to sever the connection between sleep and underlying fear, you must first alter the mood tone of sleep. Just as you feel buoyed when you dress to go out, your mood will lift when you dress for bed. Instead of retiring in an atmosphere of dejection, you must extend to yourself a sensuous invitation to sleep. The following specific steps will induce a new, relaxed feeling:

Brush your hair before bed.

Apply a cream lotion to your arms and thighs.

Splash cologne on yourself.

Wear attractive new nightclothes.

Enhance your appearance in every possible way.

• Bearing in mind that sexual activity constitutes an affirmation of life, strengthen the bond between sex and sleep.

Engage in sexual activity whenever possible at bedtime.

Choose bedroom decorations such as paintings with sensual qualities in keeping with your own taste, whether prim or abandoned.

Unless you find sexual fantasy uncomfortably arousing, reserve the night for daydreams relating to sex.

• Change your sleep environment. Let us view your underlying, perhaps disguised fear to sleep as a response which originally developed from an association between sleep and death. Your fear response has, by this time, become embedded in the physical properties of your sleep environment. Your very bedroom serves as a stimulus complex which automatically triggers your fear. You must now attempt to weaken your fear response by disrupting the stimulus complex and thus weakening its evocative power.

> Rearrange the furniture in your bedroom. If possible, consider buying some new accessories.
>
> If you habitually sleep in the dark, switch to a night light. Change your sleep environment in every possible way.

• Give yourself a little luxury before you go to bed. Only you can specify the extravagance which will best pamper you. Some suggestions to start you thinking in the proper direction are:

> A favorite selection of music.
>
> A telephone call to someone you enjoy.
>
> An interesting magazine article set aside to read at this time.
>
> A facial treatment.
>
> A perfumed bath.
>
> A happy memory reviewed.
>
> A single delicious chocolate candy.

• Your final task is to effect a basic change in your own attitude. A particularly appropriate technique of attitude change was discovered during the Second World War. At that time, a shortage of food was anticipated. It was considered advisable to develop in the general public a taste for kidneys, liver, brains, tripe, and similar organ meats, foods consigned by popular taste to the garbage dump. In order to accomplish a change in these tastes, a small city was selected as a test site. Various propaganda methods were tried without success. Finally, a number of prominent citizens were enlisted to sell the idea to the public. They were instructed to explain to their friends and neighbors the benefits of eating organ meats, and to convince others that those meats, if correctly prepared, would be delicious and appealing. This particular propaganda technique proved the most successful of all. When records of eating habits were subsequently compiled, a significant amount of attitude change was revealed and, oddly enough, the greatest amount of attitude change by far was observed in the daily menus of the salesmen themselves. Ultimately, the project was lost in the general flurry of wartime activity, but the technique itself remains a powerful tool.

We prescribe now that you use this effective instrument to change your own attitude toward sleep, that you demonstrate to yourself the proven fact that sleep is a dynamic process during which an enormous amount of activity occurs, that it is a life-giving and vital interval, the very antithesis of the quietude of death. Compile a written or mental list of activities which are accelerated during sleep. In order to gather this material, be sure to consult once more the sections in Chapter 4 on Stage 2 and Stage 4 sleep. Select a confidant, your spouse or a friend, and describe in the greatest possible detail the vigorous body processes which are charged and discharged under the cover of sleep. Explain how sleep provides for periods of heightened activity rather than a slackening of body functions. Emphasize how active, how vibrant, how lifelike is the process of sleep. Make your presentation as interesting and as positive as possible. A most important person will be listening: you.

In summary:
- Use perfumes and lotions, or colognes and aftershaves and wear nightclothes which will help you to look and feel attractive in bed.
- Engage in sexual activity as often as possible.
- Change your sleep environment.
- Give yourself a little extra luxury at bedtime.
- Describe to another person the heightened activity which occurs during the course of sleep.

CHAPTER 8

Disorders of Sleep

It was a gentle summer night. The air was cool after the heat of the day. In the street below, a cat howled a piercing, almost human shriek. A window across the courtyard slammed shut. The howling ceased abruptly, and the night settled back into silence. Claire turned in her bed. After a few moments, she opened her eyes. A faint gleam from a streetlight floated through the window to George's slacks, hanging lopsided over the back of the chair. She looked toward George. His back was turned to her, as if even in sleep he remembered that he was angry. She, too, was angry. She turned her head toward the bedroom door. She thought that she might cry, then she made a firm decision not to cry again. It was trivial, she thought, unimportant, just irritability brought on by the heat of the day. But he was so unkind. Lying awake, thinking about George, she realized that *she wanted to eat something sweet* and she remembered the cake in the refrigerator. She sat up, put her feet on the floor, and, barefoot, went into the kitchen.

The cake was a Genoise, rich with butter and eggs, topped by thick whipped cream and strawberries. I'm hungry, she thought, *hungry for something sweet*. She cut a slice of the cake. She was slim in spite of her occasional cravings for sweets. Her hair was cut short and straight, giving her the appearance of a fourteen-year-old boy rather than a *twenty-five-year-old woman*. She cut another tiny slice and allowed herself to review the dinner that led to the argument.

They had been here at the house, the six of them, for a casual dinner after an afternoon at the lake. She had prepared a cold meal in advance, so she was able to relax over a Bloody Mary with the others. Ted was talking about Morocco. He had just returned from a three-week assignment there and he was exhilarated. He was saying that the climate, the terrain, the towns might have been Mexico, they were so alike. If it were not for the caftans, the djellabas, and the Arabic lettering on the buildings, he would have thought he was in Mexico.

Claire wondered why other people's trips were so boring. *She felt sleepy. She was always sleepy these days.* Today, she mused, her sleepiness might be due to the sun and the swim in the lake. She tried to listen to Ted. He was talking about sheep, the sheep and lambs everywhere in the Moroccan countryside. She thought that she would surely fall asleep.

"Claire?" George awakened her. "Do we have any limes? I need a lime." He was mixing a gin and tonic for Linda. Claire felt too tired to move. Nobody seemed to have noticed her little nap.

"In the refrigerator," Claire replied. She watched George go for the lime. Then she turned back to Ted, still talking about Morocco.

Later at dinner, somehow she lost the thread of the conversation. Helen reached for a stalk of celery. Claire watched Helen's hand. The nail polish was chipped on her middle nail, and she wore a gold ring on her little finger. David poured ice water from a pitcher into his glass. He said something about bulbs. She did not know whether he meant electric bulbs or flower bulbs. *She stood up abruptly and walked out of the room.* When they looked for her twenty minutes later, they found her in the living room. *The bookcase had been emptied of all the books on the lower shelves. Piles of books were stacked on the chairs and on the sofa. She was sitting on the floor reading.*

They left early, as soon as dinner was over. Linda and Helen offered to help with the dishes but she preferred to clean up alone after everyone had left. When they were gone, George went into the bedroom without a word. She sighed, then placed the dishes in the dishwasher. She was wrapping the leftover cold chicken when George returned to the kitchen.

"What is the matter with you?" he demanded angrily. "What kind of a stunt was that?"

"Stop yelling," she answered.

"Why did you do that? You insulted them. Why did you want to insult them? We were having a nice evening, and you insulted them for no reason. Are you crazy?"

"I don't know why," she said.

He stormed out of the kitchen, slamming the door.

When she had put the kitchen in order, she went to bed. George seemed to be sleeping. She lay on her back, eyes wide open, staring at the ceiling. It seemed a very long time. As she lay there, *she saw a nurse in a white uniform, holding a paper cup in her hand.* Strange. So strange. Instead of coming through the doorway, *the nurse walked right through the wall. She stood at Claire's bedside for a minute, then she turned and walked out through the doorway of the bedroom.*

Sunday morning. Even before she was fully awake she could tell that it was Sunday. Sunday felt different, sounded different from other mornings. George was not in his bed. She stumbled out of bed, brushed her teeth, and walked to the kitchen for a cup of coffee. George was reading the magazine section of the Sunday *Times.* He did not look up. He had brewed a pot of coffee. She took a cup and saucer from the cabinet and poured coffee for herself. Still at the stove, she said to George, "I don't know why I did it." Then she took her coffee to the kitchen table and sat down.

"What do you mean, you don't know?" George accused. His voice was loud. Suddenly she felt frightened. The cup fell out of her hand to the floor. She tried to bend over to pick up the pieces. *She could not move. She could not move at all.* It was like a nightmare, one of those terrifying nightmares in which you must run or fight to save youself, but you cannot move a muscle.

George stared blankly at the puddle of coffee on the floor, then at Claire.

"What happened?" he said.

She could not answer.

He walked over to her, and stood beside her, looking at her. Then he touched her face. His touch freed her. She could move again. She stood up, put her face against his chest for comfort, and started to cry.

Claire was suffering from her first attack of a disorder called *narcolepsy*, a condition characterized by brief attacks of deep sleep. The italicized portions in the story you have just read are relevant to narcoleptic symptoms. We are going to explain the significance of these symptoms, so that medical help may be sought where it is necessary. First, a word of caution is in order. You must beware of the medical student syndrome, the reactions of a novice to a list of symptoms. The first-year medical student tends to find in himself all of the diseases he studies. Like medical students, we have all experienced, in mild form, symptoms associated with serious disease. Pathological conditions are often merely intense manifestations of normal processes. Diagnostic error is easy. Remember that the incidence of narcolepsy in the general population is infrequent, less than one-tenth of one percent. The odds are high that neither you nor anyone you know suffers from narcolepsy.

Mindful of this warning, let us return now to the portions of Claire's case which are relevant to narcolepsy.

1. *hungry for something sweet* ... Narcoleptic patients may report a craving for sweet foods. Healthy people also may have a craving for sweets, and it is important to remember that this craving is only one in a constellation of symptoms. The underlying cause of the craving for sweets in association with narcolepsy is currently under scientific investigation.

2. *twenty-five-year-old woman* ... Narcolepsy first becomes a serious complaint between the fifteenth and twenty-fifth year for most victims. In children, narcolepsy often remains undetected, although it interferes with the child's ability to learn. The narcoleptic child is usually considered a dull child. Persistent sleepiness in a child should be brought to the attention of a physician who is a specialist in sleep disorders.

3. *She felt sleepy* ... Excessive daytime sleepiness is the crucial symptom of narcolepsy. In severe cases, inappropriate sleep episodes are reported. Patients may fall asleep at any time: while eating, during an exciting motion picture, and quite frequently during sexual intercourse. Generally, however, narcoleptics report merely a general prevailing

need to sleep, with an intensification of sleepiness in boring, soporific situations.

4. *She stood up abruptly and walked out of the room . . . The bookcase
   had been emptied . . .* Claire's conduct is an example of
   automatic behavior. Automatic behavior or "blackout" is
   found in fifty percent of narcoleptic patients. These black-
   outs may last for a few seconds, as when Claire lost the
   thread of the conversation at the dinner table, or they may
   last for several hours. During prolonged episodes of automatic behavior, the victim may carry out any habitual
   action. Patients have been known to drive automobiles
   during these attacks. One woman went through the habitual work of cleaning her kitchen. She put her dishes in the
   clothes washer and then turned it on!

5. *she saw a nurse in a white uniform. . . .* Hypnagogic hallucinations, which also occur in non-narcoleptic individuals, are
   particularly vivid during narcoleptic attacks. They may be
   frightening as well as realistic. Numerous case studies
   show the same terrifying characters reenacting the same
   dramas in the hypnagogic experiences of the narcoleptic.

6. *She could not move . . .* Episodes of muscular weakness occur
   in almost all victims of narcolepsy. These episodes are
   usually precipitated by strong emotion. They may take the
   from of inability to move or, on occasion, total collapse.
   Even when they drop to the floor, patients remain fully
   conscious.

The nature of the narcoleptic sleep attack was only recently
discovered with the use of the EEG in the sleep laboratory. The
narcoleptic, instead of making a slow seventy- to ninety-minute
transition from wakefulness down through the four sleep stages
and then back up to dream sleep, enters dream sleep directly from
a waking state. The various symptoms which are associated with
narcolepsy seem to result from a disorder of the sleep stage
process, with muscular weakness normally associated with dream
sleep appearing when the patient is awake and, conversely, waking phenomena occurring during sleep.

The critical signposts, those which require medical evaluation, are a history of extreme daytime sleepiness, or of uncon-

trollable episodes of sleep, plus a history of brief incidents of either muscular weakness or paralysis. Because narcolepsy is a disorder of sleep, it is wise to seek diagnosis for suspected narcolepsy at a sleep laboratory, where diagnosis and treatment will be handled by experts in the sleep field.

They had been married for two months. Bill was twenty-four years old and Annie was twenty-one. Bill tipped his chair back. He yawned. He watched Annie put each item in its place before they went to bed. Her neatness amazed him. "A place for each thing and each thing in its place," she once said, sounding like a prim schoolteacher. He would have preferred a little less orderliness in the apartment, especially when she asked him to put his shoes in the closet or to hang up his jacket. But still, he thought, she really was not at all prim, and he liked to come home in the evening to the serenity of the living room and to her careful preparations for dinner.

"Coming to bed?" he asked.

The room was in order. "Yes," she said.

They were both late the next morning. Bill made the coffee while Annie toasted corn muffins.

"I couldn't find the coffee pot," he said. "Why did you put it in the refrigerator?"

"I didn't," she said.

"That's where it was."

"Don't be a wise guy," she answered.

"I mean it."

"It's late," she said. "We'd better hurry."

A few days later, Annie asked him, "Did we leave the TV set turned on last night?"

"Not that I remember," Bill said.

"It woke me up at six-thirty," Annie told him. "I heard voices in the other room."

"I don't remember anything about it," Bill said.

"Neither do I." Annie dismissed the incident.

Three or four weeks passed. Then, one morning, Bill went into the kitchen and found a puddle of milk on the kitchen floor. The milk carton was lying on its side in the refrigerator, with milk dripping over a bowl of apples and into the vegetable crisper at the bottom of the refrigerator.

"Annie," he called. "Look at this."

"I'm dressing," she called back.

"Come here right away," he insisted.

She ran in quickly and stood looking at the spilled milk, nonplussed. Finally, she murmured, "That's weird. What could have happened?"

"Do you walk in your sleep?" he asked.

"No," she said. Then after a long pause, she added, "Do you?"

"I have an uncle who walks in his sleep," Bill said, "but not me. *I talked in my sleep after an automobile accident,* but I was twelve then." He was silent, remembering. "My mother said that *it took a long time before I was properly housebroken,* but that's it." He blotted up the milk on the floor with paper towels.

Annie went to the kitchen window. The window opened on a fire escape. "Bill," she said, "the window is unlocked."

"That is weird," he agreed. He felt a chill of horror. "It's bizarre." Annie turned the latch, locking the window. She shivered. They cleaned the floor and the refrigerator before they left for their offices.

Thereafter, Annie and Bill were careful to keep the kitchen window locked, but aside from that precaution, they no longer referred to the incident. Two months later on a Monday morning, Bill found the living room lamp lit. He was sure the room had been dark when they went to bed. He checked the kitchen window. It was locked. He went to the living room window. It was unlocked and slightly ajar from the top. He looked down. The window was six stories above a courtyard. He put his head out to look at the fire escape. It was fully ten feet away from the open window, so that their living room seemed clearly unavailable to any ordinary burglar. *He shook his head in disbelief.* That night after he was sure that Annie was asleep, he slipped out of bed. Quietly, he tiptoed barefoot into the kitchen. He unlocked the window and opened it from the bottom. He unlocked both of the living room windows and opened them, too. Then he sat down in the dark to watch and wait. Although he dozed from time to time, he was awake for most of the night. When he saw the sky begin to lighten, he locked the windows and went back to bed. An hour later, when he checked, everything was in its place exactly as before they went to bed.

He did the same thing one night the next week, and then

again in the week that followed. Each time, nothing was disturbed in the morning. He gave up his attempt to solve the mystery.

On Thanksgiving night, Annie awakened in the middle of the night. She lay still, allowing languid thoughts to drift through her mind. After a little while, she became aware that something was missing. A full minute passed before she realized that she didn't hear Bill breathing beside her. She looked toward his bed. Then she moved closer and stretched out her hand. He was not in his bed. She swung her feet to the floor and stood up, instantly alert. She called to him. There was no answer. She ran to the living room, to the kitchen, the bathroom, switching on lights as she ran. She looked at the kitchen clock. It read 2:46. She ran to the front door. It was wide open. She closed it and dashed frantically to the bedroom for her slippers. She stopped at the hall closet for her coat, then, slipping the lock so that she could get back into the apartment, she rushed out into the hall.

She paused for a moment. She had really known it all the time. Somewhere in the back of her mind, she had known. She climbed the single flight of steps to the roof of the apartment house, and pushed open the heavy fire door. She stopped to prop it open. Then she stepped outside into the chilly autumn night and looked around. At first, she saw nothing. Then, in the far corner of the roof, something moved. "Bill," she called softly, "Bill, this way." The figure moved toward her. Her heart was pounding in her ears. He approached slowly. *His eyes were open. He stared at her, almost unseeing.* She reached out to take his hand in hers. Meekly, he allowed her to lead him, looking neither right nor left. Inside the door to the roof, Annie placed Bill's free hand on the bannister, and then pulled his other hand gently. Still staring straight ahead, Bill descended the stairs automatically. She took him into the apartment and put him to bed, still fast asleep.

Bill was suffering from *somnambulism,* or sleepwalking. Studies have established that somnambulism is found primarily in males. Although basically an ailment of childhood, somnambulistic behavior also appears in the young adult population, and occasionally mature adults also suffer this sleep disorder. The italicized portions of Bill's story are relevant to somnambulism.

1. *I had an uncle who walked in his sleep* . . . Sleepwalking generally appears in the family history of affected persons.

2. *I cried out in my sleep after an automobile accident* . . . The malady is sometimes associated with trauma. Victims usually display other sleep disturbances as well.

3. *it took a long time before I was housebroken* . . . Enuresis is sometimes associated with sleepwalking.

4. *He shook his head in disbelief* . . . Somnambulists do not remember their sleepwalking exploits. The episodes occur during Stage 3 and Stage 4 non-dream sleep. Before the advent of the EEG as an agent for the study of sleep, it was generally believed that sleepwalkers acted out their dreams. EEG studies negated this plausible but erroneous notion. The somnambulistic experience does not register in the conscious thoughts of the sleepwalker.

5. *His eyes were open* . . . Although the sleepwalker can see, awareness during episodes is at a low level.

Contrary to popular belief, the sleepwalker does not perform acts of great skill in avoiding danger. In spite of folklore, which attributes to the somnambulist remarkable feats of balance over the edge of a precipice or chasm, the sleepwalker is actually in danger, even in commonplace situations which present no threat under waking conditions. If you walk in your sleep, it is necessary to safeguard against danger by locking the bedroom door in such a manner that it cannot be opened automatically. Medical assistance should be secured from a sleep expert. Drugs which decrease Stage 3 and Stage 4 sleep have been used successfully to decrease or eliminate sleepwalking episodes.

Next to her, in the double bed that he had carefully reserved, *Howard was snoring.* His breath rattled in his throat. She heard him gurgle. *His arms flailed as he turned over.* Then he was silent. Jane got out of bed and groped on the floor of the hotel room for her nightgown. She found it in a little heap of satin, and holding it up in the dark, she slipped it over her head. She was fifty-two years old. She was tall and vivacious, and since her husband's death two years earlier, she had been lonely. Her arms were bare. Impossible to find her robe in the strange darkness of the hotel room, but she remembered an extra blanket at the foot of the bed. She slid her hand along the edge of the bed until she felt the blanket, and when her eyes became accustomed to the darkness, she sat in the chair with the blanket wrapped around her shoulders. The sexual revolution, she said to herself, is for the birds. She pulled her heels up onto the chair and hugged her knees. Let's face it, Jane, she continued, you're not the flaming liberal you thought you were. For all your progressive talk about other revolutions, this is the only revolution that ever hit you squarely between the eyes, and you, Jane, are a Tory. You are a White Russian. You are a Falangist in the war for sexual liberation.

He snored again and muttered in his sleep. His snore was not like other snores she had heard. First he hissed a whispered, interrupted gasp. Then he rasped a long gargle of a snore. She shuddered. This, she thought, is the pits. He sounded more like an animal than a man. Not an ape, she thought, an ape doesn't snore. Not a camel. What kind of an animal, she mused. Not a lion, surely not a king of the jungle. Not a tiger. No, not a supple, silent tiger. A horse. Yes, a horse. Oh, my God, she thought, I've mated with a horse. She began to laugh silently, shaking with laughter in the dark. It's a damned good thing for you, my dear girl, that you can't conceive, she said to herself. Otherwise you might have been delivered of a foal. She was immediately contrite. She stopped laughing.

Don't be mean, Jane, she told herself. He had really been sweet before he fell asleep and started to snore. He had been patiently, tenderly sweet. She had really liked him. She had been almost ready to begin to think about loving him, until she awakened to the grunting, gurgling noises of his sleep.

They had met four months earlier at a dinner arranged by a friend to introduce them to each other. The evening was awkward, and she promised herself that night that she would never yield to such an embarrassment again. Four other couples, all married, observed their every move throughout the entire evening. To make matters even worse, Howard was not particularly attentive. She went home feeling like a wallflower after a prom. But to her surprise, he telephoned the next night. He was tall, with a big frame. Actually, *he was overweight,* but he carried his weight well. He, too, was widowed. They went out together every week for four months. She was beginning to wonder if he was impotent, when he told her he was taking her to a little place in the country for the weekend.

His snoring was irregular. Sometimes he seemed to stop breathing, then he would gasp and turn restlessly, murmuring, or flinging his arms out as he turned. Impossible for her to sleep. There was nowhere she could go in the middle of the night. She could hardly awaken him and demand to be taken home. She returned to the bed, covering her ears with the pillow and the blanket.

He had been considerate, even romantic. They had dined leisurely at a table overlooking the canal. Later he was loving and perhaps just a little bit shy. They were both a little bit shy, she remembered. She had fallen asleep happy. Now, with the pillow and blanket over her ears, smiling faintly, she fell asleep again.

She awakened with a cry of pain even before she knew what had happened. Her head felt as if it had exploded. A sharp circle of pain radiated from her left eye to her ear on one side, and across the bridge of her nose on the other side. She began to cry aloud. He heard her and jumped up. "What happened?" he asked switching on the light.

"My head. My eye," she moaned, rocking back and forth in bed. Gently, he pulled her hands away from her face. "It's swelling," he said. He ran into the bathroom returning immediately with a cold, wet towel. "Did I . . ." he asked, patting the towel against her eye.

"You hit me," she whimpered.

"I was asleep," he repeated miserably. "I didn't mean to. You know I didn't mean to."

"Take me home," she pleaded. "I want to go home."

They dressed quickly, in silence, and left despondently. He sent flowers later that same day. His card read simply "Howard." He telephoned every night for a week, but she was always too busy to talk for more than a minute. Finally, he stopped calling. In odd moments of loneliness, she felt a tinge of regret.

Then one evening, months later, the telephone rang. It was Howard.

"Hello, Jane," he said.

"How are you, Howard?"

"Jane," he said, "have you ever heard of something called apnea?"

"What is it called?"

"Apnea. Sleep apnea."
"No. I don't think I've ever heard of it."
"May I come and tell you about it?"
She paused a long moment.
"Jane?" he repeated timidly.
"All right, Howard," she said. "Come on over."

Howard was suffering from a syndrome called *sleep apnea*. The victim of sleep apnea is able to breathe regularly only when awake. Consequently, sleep is punctuated by momentary awakenings between breaths. Patients may awaken as many as five hundred times during the night. They return to sleep immediately, only to awaken again sixty to one hundred seconds later. Naturally, this constantly interrupted sleep is not restful, and, although completely unaware of the reason, the victim feels tired and sleepy during the day. Those who remember their waking moments often do not realize that they slept at all. They complain of insomnia. Others, who do not recall waking, also feel sleepy during the day, but their complaint is too much sleep. It is also possible that people who suffer apnea are unable to specify the nature of their discomfort, and do not seek the necessary assistance at all. The italicized portions of Howard's story are relevant to sleep apnea.

1. *Howard was snoring* ... During sleep, the respiratory apparatus of those afflicted with apnea ceases to function, and the throat alters its normal tone, thus choking off the flow of air. During the breathless phase of the breathing cycle, carbon dioxide accumulates in the blood, while at the same time, oxygen in the blood is depleted. However, a natural safety mechanism awakens the sleeper, who then promptly draws a deep breath. The throat regains its normal tone. The unpleasant gasping, gurgling, and snoring aspirations result from the rush of air against the slightly collapsed muscles of the throat.

2. *His arms flailed as he turned over* ... Flailing, thrashing, and restless movements often accompany the tortured struggle for air.

3. *he was overweight* ... Apnea attacks mainly middle-aged

men who are overweight. At the Stanford University Sleep Disorders Clinic, the average age of patients is fifty-two years.

Although sleep apnea was described in conjunction with too much sleep in 1965, it was rediscovered as an underlying cause of insomnia complaint at the Stanford University Sleep Disorders Clinic in 1972.

At present, the cause of the illness is unknown. Some experts believe that apnea may be present at birth. A major investigatory effort is currently directed to the possible relationship of apnea to crib death in infants.

Sleep apnea is treated by various drugs and by a simple surgical procedure which allows the patient to breathe easily and silently during sleep through a small valve inserted into the trachea. However, before corrective measures can be initiated, precise diagnosis is an essential precondition. According to Dr. William C. Dement, founder and director of the Stanford University Sleep Disorders Program, "Unfortunately, only a handful of physicians are aware of the existence and ramifications of sleep apnea." When one considers that the syndrome in connection with insomnia was first recognized and described as recently as 1972, it is no wonder that most physicians have had no experience with this malady as such. Therefore, the same advice which applies to other sleep disorders applies even more strongly to possible sleep apnea. Diagnosis and treatment should be undertaken by sleep experts at a hospital-associated sleep laboratory.

If you suspect that you suffer apnea, you may wish to consult your own physician for preliminary guidance. Do not be shy about sharing the supposedly sacrosanct medical prerogative of diagnosis. In June 1978 the *Journal of the American Medical Association* featured an article which stated that most physicians are deficient in sleep information. Classes and education for practicing physicians were still, at that date, in the planning stage. You have a great deal of information at your disposal, and you know more about your own condition than anyone else. Feel free to use your knowledge in offering relevant facts to your doctor. She or he will probably welcome your contribution. If, after a few cursory questions, your doctor simply reaches for a prescription pad, your complaints are probably not receiving the careful evaluation they deserve. Feel absolutely free to explain to your physician that sleep disorders do not respond to either patent medicines or prescription drugs. You will not be out of order—you will be repeating the advice tendered by sleep researchers themselves to practicing physicians. As a special warning, it is crucial to bear in mind that under no circumstances should you use any kind of pills if there is any possibility you suffer apnea. Pills can be fatal in apnea cases.

For suspected sleep apnea, keep the following clues in mind:

Constant fatigue, and especially fatigue upon awakening in the morning, may indicate sleep apnea.

Although apnea attacks mostly men, women may also suffer this disorder, and consequently women should not dismiss the possibility of apnea merely because of their sex.

Although apnea victims are often overweight, thinner subjects are appearing with increasing frequency. The fact that your weight is normal does not rule out the possibility of apnea.

Many victims display an absolutely normal breathing function while awake. For complete accuracy, tests for apnea must be conducted while the patient sleeps.

Loud snoring is the critical symptom. If you suffer any form of insomnia, and you learn from any source that your snoring is unusually loud, you should check out the possibility of apnea.

Thomas Roth, sleep researcher of Detroit's Henry Ford Hospital, suggests that physicians lend tape recorders to their patients to be placed close to the bed and turned on before retiring. You may wish to adopt this excellent idea, so that you can bring an objective record of your breathing pattern to your doctor for appraisal and possible determination to refer you to a sleep laboratory for further evaluation.

The mysterious actions of somnambulism and night terrors, as well as the prosaic but frustrating disability of *enuresis* (bedwetting) all occur during Stage 4 sleep, the deepest of all the sleep stages. The victims of all of these disturbances are totally amnesiac for the events which they acted out during the night. Victims of night terrors do not recall the reason for their fright, and somnambulists remember nothing of their exploits, even when they have performed complicated maneuvers. Enuretics may believe that urination was prompted by a dream, but studies reveal that the dream and urination do not occur at the same time. Urination usually precedes the dream, but on occasion it occurs after the dream is completed. When urination precedes the dream, it is believed that the sensation of wet clothing precipitates a dream of urination. When urination follows the dream, it is believed that bladder pressure causes both the dream and, later, the act.

Before the advent of the EEG, a facile, intuitive explanation lay readily available to physician and layman alike. It was generally thought that the sleeper was going through the motions of his dream. But now the contradictory evidence of the EEG is irrefutable. No dreams underlie the terror, the walking, or the bed-wetting which occur during sleep.

The actual incidence of enuresis is unknown. One wonders how many people suffer in embarrassed silence without comfort or assistance. In a 1957 study of five hundred children between the ages of four and fourteen, the reported incidence was twenty-two percent. Among the victims of enuresis, males predominate. It is estimated that two men in one hundred are enuretic. Unfortunately, the malady carries a stigma which is undeserved. Like the child, the enuretic adult is physically unable to stop the spontaneous discharge of urine during the night. Nevertheless, we tend to blame him for his failure to master the control which we, who are not so afflicted, have achieved automatically in the natural course of maturation. Meanwhile, the stigma of enuresis is accompanied by a strong sense of shame which envelops the victim. At one time, we treated Michael, a shy, enuretic fourteen-year-old boy. Before his first session, he doodled as he sat in the waiting room. When he entered the office, he was still holding his sheet of paper in his hand. He had drawn a skillful rendition of a boy. "Who is that?" we asked.

Michael blushed. "It's me," he said.

The picture told the story of Michael's self-esteem. The boy he had sketched was only two inches high.

Until recently, enuresis was generally attributed to psychological causes. The act of bed-wetting was viewed as symbolic, an expression of the male's unresolved competition with his father for the love of his mother. This interpretation is currently losing advocates, although it is still favored in some quarters. As to the physical characteristics of enuretics, detailed study has shown dramatically that enuretic children sleep more deeply than other children, that their bladder capacity is smaller, that arousal from sleep takes a longer period of time, and that the disturbance, like other Stage 4 disturbances, tends to run in families. The same findings presumably apply to the enuretic adult.

Enuresis has been successfully treated with various methods. One frequently successful procedure utilizes apparatus which sounds a buzzer and delivers a mild shock the moment moisture penetrates the bed sheet. The sleeper is, of course, immediately awakened. Continued application of the buzzer-shock combination reduces the already minute interval between the buzzer and awakening. Thus, if initially the sleeper awakens in thirty seconds, after a period of this buzzer treatment awakening occurs after only fifteen seconds. Finally, and ideally, the enuretic becomes conditioned, and awakens before the buzzer sounds and in time to get to the bathroom. At this point, the enuretic is cured.

Additionally, a number of drugs are in current use. One drug was administered originally as an antidepressant, in an attempt to alleviate enuresis by promoting a relaxed mood, and it was proven effective. Then, an interesting side effect of this drug was discovered. In addition to elevating the patient's mood, the drug actually increases bladder capacity, thereby lessening the pressure which produces enuresis. Another drug decreases the amount of Stage 4 sleep, thus reducing the probability of bladder discharge during this sleep stage. Most children master bladder control eventually during the course of their normal development. For the parents of children who achieve control later than age four, it is important that they minimize their own anxiety, as well as the anxiety and guilt of the child. As for adults still struggling with enuresis, medical assistance is recommended. New studies, new experiments, new treatments are being reported periodically. If enuresis is your problem, and if you have not thus far been helped, do not give up. Continue to consult reputable physicians and keep informed of new methods of treatment. To repair the problem of damaged self-esteem, psychotherapy is indicated.

Night terrors, *pavor nocturnus* in children and *incubus* in adults, also emanate from deep Stage 4 sleep. They occur far less frequently than enuresis and less frequently than somnambulism. All three are sometimes seen in the same individuals. The night terror differs from the nightmare in that the nightmare, which arises out of dream sleep, ends with a sudden arousal and with a memory of events in the frightening dream. Even two-year-old children often describe their nightmares: "A bear was in my bed" or "There's a big doggie in the room." In contrast, the night terror involves *no dream at all*, and the terrified arousal, far from being abrupt, is prolonged. The child shrieks from the depths of sleep and will often sit up, eyes glazed, breathing heavily, and screaming in terror. Efforts to comfort or to awaken the child are equally unsuccessful. The child emerges from sleep several minutes later. No memory of the event can be elicited. The child is calm, unaffected by the preceding terror. Only the parents are visibly shaken. These episodes usually disappear by the age of five. No treatment is administered. Some adults experience a similar type of Stage 4 behavior, awakening from deep non-dream sleep with feelings of terror. Heart rate and breathing are rapid, as in fright. There is no memory of a precipitating dream and yet, unlike the child, the adult suffers, for a time, a sense of fear.

Incubus, or night terrors in adults, is considered to be rare. The actual incidence of the disturbance is probably unknown. It is only natural to confuse the night terror which arises out of Stage 4 non-dream sleep with the nightmare which springs from dream sleep. It is safe to surmise that many victims suffer in silence. This is unfortunate. Fear is a painful emotion. Everyone is familiar with the debilitating effects of fright. If you experience night terrors, you should make every possible effort to obtain relief. Take your problem to a sleep laboratory, where experts will be available to help you.

In summary, the disorders of sleep call for medical treatment at different levels. Enuresis and somnambulism can be adequately handled by a competent physician, while narcolepsy, night terrors, and sleep apnea require the apparatus and the expertise available at a sleep laboratory. A list of sleep laboratories appears on pages 211-213.

CHAPTER 9
Medication

At their worst, prescription sleep drugs are fatal. At their best, they furnish only temporary relief. Between these two extremes, they may lead to addiction; they may lead to dependency, a milder but still serious form of addiction; they decrease rather than increase sleep; and they always interfere with the natural functioning of the nervous system.

Sleep medications achieve their effect by blocking pathways to your brain. All information from the world outside of yourself is received by sensory receptors: eyes for sight, ears for sound, tongue for taste, nose for odor, and skin for touch and temperature. These few channels comprise our receptive equipment. Without these sensory channels, we are literally cut off from the world, we are isolated, we are insensate. All of the messages received by our sense organs are fed along microscopic threadlike neurons into the central nervous system. Sleeping pills create their soporific effect by blocking these incoming pathways. With the block in place, sensations of all kinds are reduced, whereupon sleep follows with relative ease. The sedative-hypnotics, which is the term for sleeping pills, are often merely milder versions of the hypnotics administered to block pain during surgery. Putting it briefly, they are strong, strong medicine.

Sleep preparations are classified on the basis of their chemical composition. Historically, the barbiturates compounded of barbituric acid preceded most other sedative hypnotics now in use. When introduced in 1903, they were received as a boon, a valuable weapon in the armamentarium of the war against sleeplessness and emotional turmoil. (Heroin, incidentally, was received at its introduction with equivalent optimism.) When a barbiturate is swallowed for the first time, sleep usually follows within twenty minutes. Emotions are soothed even more rapidly. Barbiturates depress heart rate, respiration, and blood pressure. They suppress dream sleep as well. A considerable time after the initial welcome accorded to barbiturates, cases of toxic reactions and of barbiturate addiction appeared in physicians' waiting rooms and in hospital beds with increasing and alarming frequency. Addiction to barbiturates can be incurred with absolute innocence. Pills of high dosage, taken regularly, silently create an addiction. Withdrawal from barbiturate addiction exposes the unwitting addict to the possibility of acute, almost unbearable discomfort, manifested in rages, attacks of anxiety, thought disorders, hallucination, high fever, coma, and even death. Barbiturate withdrawal imposes even greater danger than withdrawal from heroin.

Barbiturates are dangerous. The dangers have been repeatedly called to the attention of the medical profession. In 1974, the American Medical Association cautioned its members to avoid barbiturate prescriptions, except for the most severe symptoms. In the same year, the *New England Journal of Medicine* declared that, "The barbiturate hypnotics have been rendered obsolete by pharmacologic progress and deserve speedy oblivion." And yet, even now, long after these warnings, the prescriptions continue. In 1977, in complete disregard of danger to patients, a shocking total of sixteen million, four hundred and sixty-seven thousand prescriptions for barbiturates were written.

For your guidance, a list of popular barbiturates follows. Examine the list carefully, and check it against your own prescription.

Trade Name	Generic Name
Amytal	amobarbital
Amytal Sodium	amobarbital
A.P.B.	phenobarbital
Butisol	sodium butabarbital

Carbrital	pentobarbital sodium and cabroma combined
Dularin-TH	sodium butabarbital
Eskabarb	phenobarbital
Hyptran	secobarbital
Luminal	phenobarbital
Nebralin Tablets	pentobarbital
Nembutal	pentobarbital
Qui-A-Zone III	butabarbital and phenobarbital combined
Seco-8-Capsules	secobarbital
Seconal	secobarbital
Sedadrops	phenobarbital
Solfoton	phenobarbital
Stental	phenobarbital
Tuinal	amobarbital and secobarbital combined

Hospital personnel are familiar with the patients who reveal an inordinate need for their sleeping pills. No matter what the cause of the hospitalization, the patient keeps inquiring about the sleep tablets. Even the volunteer workers who serve fruit juice and deliver newspapers to the patients soon learn to recognize the middle-class, often middle-aged sleeping pill junkie. Sadly enough, no matter how cultured, how well spoken, no matter how respectable the patient, the contempt which is accorded to addicts generally is directed to the barbiturate addict as well. If you are taking a barbiturate, even occasionally, do you really wish to continue?

In the 1950's a class of new non-barbiturate sedative-hypnotic was introduced. History, true to form, repeated itself. These new drugs were hailed as the new saviors of sleep and warriors against anxiety. They include:

Trade Name	Generic Name
Deprol	meprobamate
Doriden	glutethimide
Equanil	meprobamate
Meprospan	meprobamate
Milpath	meprobamate
Milpram	meprobamate
Miltown	meprobamate
Noludar	methyprylon

Placidyl	ethchlorvynol
Quaalude	methaqualone
SK-Bamate	meprobamate
Sopor	methaqualone
Valmid	ethinamate

These hypnotics comprise a large new group of non-barbiturate sleep drugs. Although hailed at their introduction, some twenty-odd years later, in 1977, James R. Cooper, M.D., of the National Institute on Drug Abuse, referred to some of these non-barbiturate compounds in the following explicit language: ". . . [They] may pose even more serious problems in the area of toxicity than the barbiturate drugs they were intended to replace." Not only are these drugs potentially toxic, but, ironically enough, while their danger persists as a continuing threat to the user, their effective power as a sleeping pill is quickly lost.

As a matter of fact, most of the prescription pills, both the barbiturates and the non-barbiturate drugs, lose their effectiveness after only two weeks of regular use. Thus, a number of popular sleep drugs were laboratory-tested by Anthony Kales, M.D., and his associates at the sleep facility of Pennsylvania State University. They included these drugs or their equivalent:

Trade Name	Generic Name
A. Barbiturates	
Nembutal	pentobarbital
Seconal	secobarbital
B. Non-Barbiturates	
Aquachloral	chloral hydrate
Doriden	glutethimide
Kessodrate	chloral hydrate
Noctec	chloral hydrate
Placidyl	etchlorvynol
Parest	methaqualone hydrochloride
Quaalude	methaqualone
Sopor	methaqualone

All drugs tested were found to be ineffective within two weeks of nightly use. These findings received wide publicity in the popular press as well as in medical literature. Nevertheless, with utter disregard of the evidence, physicians continue to prescribe these drugs for sleep-related problems. In 1977, an astronomical total of twenty-one million non-barbiturate sleeping pill prescriptions were written. Not only are they prescribed, but they are prescribed in amounts which carry the user well past any possibility of a therapeutic effect. A national accounting revealed that sedatives were prescribed at an average rate of forty pills per prescription. How many useless, possibly harmful pills did you pay for and ingest?

If you take a sleep medication on a regular basis, at best you may feel that it induces sleep quickly. In all other respects, it exerts a deleterious rather than a beneficial effect upon your sleep. All evidence shows that you would sleep more restfully without medication. Continuous use of sleeping pills aggravates insomnia. A new syndrome, *drug-dependence insomnia,* was described in 1974 by Dr. Kales and his associates. The study was prompted by the complaints of insomniacs who, after using prescribed sleeping pills for prolonged periods, did not receive relief. The study used two groups of patients. The experimental group consisted of patients who had been taking prescribed sleeping pills for insomnia for periods of up to ten years. Their sleep was compared to that of a control group of patients who were not taking any medication. Results showed that the drug users dream less, sleep less, and also wake for longer periods during the night than the victims of insomnia who do not take drugs. The researchers, in their report which appeared in the *Journal of the American Medical Association* in 1974, concluded that "The results showed that all of the chronic drug patients had as great or greater difficulty in falling asleep or staying asleep, or both, when compared to insomniac controls who were not taking drugs."

The drug-dependence insomnia syndrome is a merry-go-round. First, the patient sleeps poorly, and for an inadequate amount of time. Administration of a drug then improves the quality and the quantity of sleep, but soon the drug loses its potency and, in spite of continued use of the drug, the patient returns to the original deficient quality and quantity sleep condition. The process, unfortunately, does not stop at this point. The decline continues so that now, even with the drug, sleep falls to a level which is actually lower than the original pre-drug quantity of nightly sleep. At this point, the patient is faced with a difficult choice. Some manage to escape. They stop taking the drug. Others continue to drug themselves with pills, which, while ineffective, exert a destructive influence. Still others increase their dosage, only to travel the same circuit once more. They sleep less than originally, but now dependence, both psychological and physical, has established a firm grip. It is too late to jump off the merry-go-round unassisted. Withdrawal will be accompanied by severe reactions. As an extreme example, a sudden withdrawal from **Butisol Sodium** can lead to a condition resembling epilepsy. High fever, coma, and finally death are additional possibilities. Consequently, when the dependency condition is reached, gradual withdrawal under competent medical supervision is required to obtain a safe release from the drug.

Through the years, Dorothy grew aware that her sleep time was gradually diminishing, but aside from an occasional tranquilizer, she avoided medication. She developed the custom of visiting her doctor once each year, in December, for a general examination. One particular year, after the physical examination had been completed, she dressed and entered the consulting room as usual. Her doctor leaned back in his high leather chair, looked at her thoughtfully, and asked, "How are you feeling?"

She hesitated. "I can't sleep," she answered, finally.

His face registered concern. "Is something bothering you?"

She had earlier decided not to discuss the problem at all, but now the words spilled out.

"My husband drinks one martini a night," she said with a little laugh. "He mixes it in a highball glass. He drinks one nine-ounce martini every night."

The doctor shook his head sympathetically. "He should cut down. That's far too much."

"He's not an alcoholic," she added quickly. "He doesn't get drunk. It's just that after he has his drink, he doesn't seem to listen."

She laughed lightly to cover her embarrassment. "He isn't missing too much when he doesn't listen to me," she added, blushing a little. Sitting there silently, she could hear her own voice as she thought her husband must hear it—complaining, perhaps even whining. She felt that he must hate her. She closed her eyes. What nonsense. He really loved her. It was just that he didn't like to listen. She thought that she might cry in a moment and so she blurted the next thought that entered her mind. "I looked at the back of my legs in the mirror," she complained. "Purple veins show. My legs look like the map of Gibraltar."

"Nothing to worry about," the doctor reassured, smiling. "Perfectly normal. Perfectly healthy."

She wanted to scream. Who wanted healthy purple veins? She used to have beautiful legs. He didn't understand. A moment later, she felt utterly foolish. Her mind flashed to the waiting room outside the panelled door, filled, she thought, with patients suffering migraine headaches, ulcers, tumors, serious disorders, while she sat consuming the doctor's valuable time with childish complaints. "My son called from Chicago," she heard herself say. "Our only child. He was married last year. He was so terribly depressed. His wife wants a divorce."

The doctor's face registered sympathy, but now his fingers began to tap restlessly on his desk. "Youngsters today," he said. "They don't know what they want." His eyes moved to the door. She could see that he was anxious to call his next patient. She felt ashamed that she had said anything at all. But he had asked her! He had tilted himself back in his judge's leather chair and had asked her, and now that she was answering his question, he was too busy to listen. She wanted to scream so that everyone in the waiting room would hear, "Why the devil did you ask me in the first place?" Instead, she slipped a Kleenex from her purse and began to cry.

He reached for his pad and wrote a prescription for **Placidyl.** "Take one every night before you go to bed," he instructed kindly. "Things have a way of getting better."

She nodded, managing half a smile as she dried her eyes.

She filled the prescription on the way home, and that night, just before bedtime, she stood in the kitchen examining the dark maroon pill. Its scent reminded her of cleaning fluid. She swallowed the capsule with a tall glass of water, and some twenty minutes later, resting gently in bed, she sank into a pleasant, comforting slumber, awakening the next morning completely refreshed and relaxed. Her husband had left for his office. A light rain was falling. Such a comfortable, cozy day. She mapped out her plans for the day: she would catch up on some reading, bake an onion quiche, write a long letter to her son. Everything seemed so much more cheerful now that she felt rested. Allen would pull out of this crisis; after all, he wasn't the only young man to be divorced; one out of three young marriages ends in divorce, she remembered, or was it one in two now? As for her husband, well, Carl had his problems, too. Maybe she talked too much at home. She resolved to say less, to be silent more frequently. She recalled the doctor's words: "Things have a way of getting better." As for the web of veins on her leg, the dryness in her skin, the slow signs of aging—"Never mind," she sighed, deciding then and there to compensate, to stand straight, to walk fast, to laugh often, to read new books, to wear the latest fashions, to adopt the newest fads, to move a little to the left politically, to overwhelm the evidence of her appearance by the stronger evidence of her personality. It was possible, she decided, it was possible, it was entirely possible.

And so now Dorothy, religiously taking her one maroon pill each night at bedtime, continued to feel cheerful and to sleep well. For ten days. Then, ever so gradually, as night followed night, Dorothy discovered herself lying awake just a little bit longer each succeeding evening, brooding, it seemed, for moments which were lengthening almost imperceptibly, falling asleep just a little bit later each night and then, most disconcerting of all, awakening before dawn unable to recapture sleep at all.

One Sunday evening, watching television with her husband in the den, she reached out and placed her hand in his. He squeezed her fingers. She waited until the commercial before she spoke.

"Allen asked me not to phone him," she said.

"When did he say that?" Carl asked curiously.

"This morning. I don't call him more than once a week," she added quickly. "I know he needs to be treated like a man, not a child. But he doesn't understand. I don't call him for him. I call him for me. I need to know that he's all right. I really need to hear his voice."

She stopped. It was so difficult to explain, to put it all into words so that Carl could understand. "I think it's all right for me to phone him once a week," she added hesitantly, waiting for Carl to confirm her tentative decision.

Carl was silent. The television commercials, following each other in rapid sequence, droned on.

"It really wouldn't make him less of a man if I telephone just once a week for my own peace of mind," she went on, again waiting for an answer from her husband.

He looked up at her now, as if suddenly aware that she was waiting for him to say something.

"It's hot in this room," he said.

With fatigue, she rose from the sofa and walked slowly to the bedroom, where, after closing the door, she fell on the bed, sobbing. Carl, unaware, remained in the den, still watching the television program. After fifteen minutes, all cried out, she sat in the living room, red-eyed, thumbing, through the day's paper. Carl retired after the ten o'clock news, mumbling a cursory "I'm tired, honey, good night." Moments later, she rose wearily and, from a closet in the kitchen, took the vial of **Placidyls,** gulping one of the pills with her usual glass of water. But this time something changed. In spite of the pill, and her fatigue, she remained wide awake, unaffected by the medication.

Wandering to the den, she switched on the television set again, clicking from one station to another. None of the programs engaged her interest. She snapped the set off and picked up the magazine section of the Sunday *New York Times.* She began reading an article on the lives of women in clubhouse politics, but she could not concentrate. Her mind wandered. To Carl. She knew that his refusal to listen involved more than preoccupation. He wanted to escape, to be somewhere else, somewhere far away, on an island in the South Seas, like Gauguin perhaps, somewhere in Tahiti. He wanted to flee, but could not, and so while his body remained, the rest of him fled. She was sorry for him. Poor Carl. Part of him somewhere else, part of him chained, imprisoned— and Allen. The most painful part of it all was her own helplessness. If only she could fix it with a Band-Aid again. But now he couldn't even talk to her. Neither of them could talk to her, not Carl, not Allen. She gathered all the sections of the Sunday *Times* and piled them neatly on the chair near the door. She picked up her empty coffee cup and carried it to the kitchen sink. She looked in the food closet for a box of crackers, and then, changing her mind, she took, instead, a second capsule of **Placidyl.**

In just a few minutes, she was comfortably in bed falling into a deep refreshing sleep.

Within three months, Dorothy required three **Placidyl** capsules in order to fall asleep, and even with three capsules she slept for no more than four hours each night. She did not dare to take four capsules, and she could not sleep at all without a pill. Dorothy had developed a classic case of drug-dependence insomnia.

In addition to barbiturate and non-barbiturate sedative-hypnotics, there are any number of *over-the-counter* (OTC) nonprescription sleep remedies. They seem, to the purchaser, to be innocuous. The nonprescription status in itself conveys the impression that the medication lacks the capacity to injure. This impression is false. If you take an OTC sleep aid, examine the label. Note the ingredients listed and then check them against the following facts.

Bromides

Ammonium bromide, potassium bromide, and sodium bromide are toxic in doses large enough to put you to sleep, and they are ineffective in smaller doses. At high concentrations in the body, bromides mimic schizophrenia.

Methapyrilene

This chemical is at the present time under suspicion as a cancer-producing agent. The Commissioner of the United States Food and Drug Administration has ordered that the drug be subjected to intensive tests. Methapyrilene, according to the FDA, cannot be considered safe. The National Cancer Institute has given high-priority status to the investigation of this OTC sleep remedy ingredient.

Scopolamine Compounds

These sleep agents are not safe at dosage levels which would prove effective in inducing nighttime sleep. Side effects of a true therapeutic dose are both unpleasant and dangerous, and can progress from constipation to complete obstruction of the bowel, and from mental confusion to serious mental disorder. The chemical occurs as a form of *belladonna*, which may also be listed as an ingredient of a sleep remedy.

A number of other ingredients which appear in sleep aids have been adjudged ineffective. Among these useless drugs are: *acetaminophen, aspirin, salicyclamide, passionflower extract,* and *thiamine hydrochloride.* Another ingredient sometimes included to improve the texture of the tablet, is *talc,* which is frequently contaminated by asbestos, a toxic substance.

The OTC sleep preparations present a double-edged disadvantage: ineffectiveness and danger. Several warnings should be kept in mind. These drugs should under no circumstances be given to children under twelve years of age. They should never be taken by pregnant women or by nursing mothers. They should not be taken in combination with other drugs. They should not be taken continuously for a period of more than two weeks. They should not be used in combination with alcohol. They should not be self-administered by a person who suffers from or suspects the presence of glaucoma, asthma, or enlargement of the prostate gland. To these warnings must be added the conclusion of the Commissioner of the Food and Drug Administration in June 1978: "The commissioner concludes that none of the submitted active ingredients can be generally recognized as safe and effective and not misbranded."

You ought to check your medicine cabinet for an OTC sleep medication. Are you one of the millions of Americans who purchase and thoughtlessly swallow over-the-counter sleeping pills?

Rather than sleeping pills or OTC preparations, many poor sleepers take tranquilizers, which are not classified as sleeping pills *per se,* but which are widely prescribed for insomnia. Most tranquilizers do not contain barbituric acid; some, however, do. The same dangers inherent in sleep barbiturates lie hidden in barbiturate tranquilizers. Three popular barbiturate tranquilizers are **Amytal, Butisol,** and **Luminal.**

Most drugs, including some of the tranquilizers, the sedative-hypnotics, and the OTC sleep remedies, suppress dream sleep. For those who decide to give up drugs, this is an important factor to be taken into consideration. The importance of any of the sleep stages, including the stage of dream sleep, is unknown. It is not possible to predict, now, the subtle effect of dream deprivation. It is clear, however, that a dream deficit is followed by a dream rebound upon cessation of drugs. Thus, when drugs which have been suppressing dreams are discontinued, the patient's sleep tends to be crowded with dreams, which may often begin immediately upon the onset of sleep instead of at the usual later time. The dreams which follow drug suppression are often turbulent. They usually carry an unpleasant flavor. Nightmares may rapidly succeed each other. The quality, duration, and intensity of rebound dreaming has led to the aptly descriptive term "storms of dreams." In order to attenuate these turbulent storms, drugs should be discontinued on a gradual schedule, with decreases in dosage instituted in small, progressive steps. Among the drugs which tend to suppress dreams are the following:

Trade Name	Generic Name
Aquachloral	chloral hydrate
Doriden	glutethimide
Kessodrate	chloral hydrate
Noctec	chloral hydrate
Noludar	methyprylon
Quaalude	methaqualone

Note: All barbiturates suppress dreams. See list of eighteen barbiturates on page 153.

Three mood elevators occasionally prescribed for sleep also tend to suppress dreams: **Ipramine, Nardil,** and **Tofranil.** To these should be added the tranquilizers **Equanil, Meprospan, Meprotabs,** and **SK-Bamate,** used as sleep medications and known for their dream-suppressing qualities.

At this point, you may disagree with information relating to dream suppression. You may be taking one of the listed medications and yet experience dreams. But the fact that you do dream while using a drug does not disprove the dream-suppression property of your drug. While you are asleep, the effect of the drug is in time dissipated, and this is followed by a natural sleep—it is at that point that you may begin to dream. Prior to dreaming, while the drug remains active, your dreams will be suppressed.

Indiscriminate use of sleep medication carries serious consequences. All of the sleep compounds perform two functions: they depress activity of the spinal cord and brain, and they induce sleep when first ingested. However, with continued use, the body becomes accustomed to the drugs and learns to resist their effects. In other words, a tolerance is developed. More exactly, two separate tolerances develop: one to the depressant effect, and another to the soporific effect. Therefore, a particular drug after continued use may fail to put you to sleep, but still, unknown to you, quiet your nervous activity. If, in order to sleep at this point, you take extra pills, as many people do, you incur the risk of a lethal depression of central nervous system activity. At the furthest extreme, it is possible for sleep medications, when taken indiscriminately and in high dosage, to produce death almost before they produce sleep. Some sleep medication fans attempt to outsmart their sleep tolerance by keeping a variety of medications on hand, and switching from one to the other on the same night or on succeeding nights. Their strategy, although clever, is futile. Cross tolerance between different drugs has been demonstrated, as well as cross tolerance even between general classes of compounds. A resistance to the sleep properties of one drug carries over, not only to other drugs of the same type, but also to other separate categories of drugs.

Historically, sleep medication was introduced by modern pharmacology in the late nineteenth century with a class of drugs which included **Noctec, Somnos,** and others which may be familiar to you, as well as **Paraldehyde,** a cyclic ether which carries an unpleasant taste and odor. These early prescriptions were followed by the barbiturates, which were in turn superseded by non-barbiturate compounds, such as **Placidyl,** and the well-known older tranquilizers, **Miltown** and **Equanil.** Two additional non-barbiturate groups were first marketed in the 1950s, and are represented by **Quaalude, Doriden,** and **Noludar.** At the very time when the adverse effects of these so-called miracle drugs were appearing, still another class of spectacular remedy was presented. These newest of our wonder medicines are still hailed as conquering heroes in some quarters. They are known as **benzodiazepines,** and subsume the tranquilizers **Librium, Valium, Serax, Tranxene,** as well as the sleep preparation **Dalmane,** which is the trade name for flurazepam. Still in the clinical trial stage, approximately fifteen more benzodiazepines are waiting in the wings for presentation, presumably with trumpets blaring, to the American public.

Many of the research tests upon the benzodiazepines have yielded optimistic results. The good tidings have been widely publicized by the drug industry and eagerly received by members of the medical profession. The number of prescriptions written for **Dalmane** since its introduction in 1970 must surely elevate the spirits of investors in Roche, the company which markets this particular drug. Total prescriptions jumped from three million in 1971, to thirteen and one-half million in 1977. It must be conceded that **Dalmane** shows several positive features when compared to other sleep medications. It is less acutely toxic. Tolerance develops at a relatively slow pace. Physical dependence seems to be less severe than the dependence produced by other drugs.

In spite of favorable reports, we are disturbed and disquieted. A review of central nervous system depressants shows that history for drugs, like history for politics, repeats itself. Each new drug appears with a fanfare, surrounded by promise, free from dependence liability. Then, as the new drugs are widely used for extended periods, the complaints of adverse reactions appear, with gradual acceleration, in the doctors' offices where the cycle first began. Even now faint rumblings can be heard in the land. EEG monitors of **Dalmane**-influenced sleep show a reduction of deep Stage 3 and Stage 4 phases. The long-term effects of deprivation of any of the sleep stages are unknown at this time, but some experts express increasing concern regarding these effects.

Another cause for uneasiness lies in the danger posed by a combination of a benzodiazepine with another central nervous system depressant, particularly alcohol. A mixed overdose of a benzodiazepine and alcohol can prove fatal. Data on the additive effect of these compounds combined with other substances is meager. Chemicals are known to be prone to synergism, an intriguing process wherein the end result equals more than the sum of the parts. In some instances, chemicals react upon each other in such a way that their combination yields a consequence which was not predictable in advance. The potential synergistic effects of benzodiazepines with other chemicals remain to be revealed.

Cases of residual drowsiness after **Dalmane** has worn off have been reported. Experimental subjects who took **Dalmane** in the usual therapeutic dose for the purpose of the test reported that they felt sleepy as long as eighteen hours later. Some elderly patients are reported to be particularly bothered by drowsiness after ingesting **Dalmane.** This suggests to us that the benzodiazepines may remain in the system for longer periods than we realize. The results of accumulation of foreign chemicals remain to be seen. It is difficult even for an optimist to envision a beneficent effect on anyone from the accumulation of artificial substances in the body.

In spite of the margin of safety generally found in the benzodiazepines to date, one contradictory and alarming report appears in the literature. Grand mal convulsions are described in a twenty-three-year-old male exposed to **diazepam** at a dosage of 10 mg. three times a day for three months. The convulsions occurred within five days following withdrawal of the drug. This young man's experience illustrates the danger inherent in regular ingestion of a central nervous system depressant of any kind, including the benzodiazepines. Physical dependence develops in all central nervous system depressants, with the possible exception of some short-acting agents, when taken in sufficient quantities and for sufficient periods of time. When we review the current literature and extract this information, alarm bells ring in our ears, lights flash in our minds' eyes, and we are impelled to communicate to you our personal sense of these formidable risks.

When your pharmacist receives a package of **Dalmane** and when your physician receives a sample of **Dalmane,** tucked into the package is a printed insert intended for the physician or the pharmacist, not for the consumer. The insert lists, along with other information, relevant facts concerning adverse reactions to the drug. The following "adverse reactions" are reprinted *verbatim* from the manufacturer's **Dalmane** sheet.

Precaution: In elderly and debilitated patients, it is recommended that the dosage initially be limited to 15 mg to preclude the development of oversedation, dizziness and/or ataxia. If Dalmane is to be combined with other drugs having known hypnotic properties or CNS-depressant effects, due consideration should be given to potential additive effects.

The usual precautions are indicated for severely depressed patients or those in whom there is any evidence of latent depression; particularly the recognition that suicidal tendencies may be present and protective measures may be necessary.

Should Dalmane be used repeatedly, periodic blood counts, and liver and kidney function tests should be performed. The usual precautions should be observed in patients with impaired renal or hepatic function.

Adverse Reactions: Dizziness, drowsiness, lightheadedness, staggering, ataxia and falling have occurred, particularly in elderly or debilitated persons. Severe sedation, lethargy, disorientation and coma, probably indicative of drug intolerance or overdosage, have been reported.

Also reported were: headache, heartburn, upset stomach, nausea, vomiting, diarrhea, constipation, gastrointestinal pain, nervousness, talkativeness, apprehension, irritability, weakness, palpitations, chest pains and genito-urinary complaints. There have also been rare occurrences of leukopenia, granulocytopenia, sweating, flushes, difficulty in focusing, blurred vision, burning eyes, faintness, hypotension, shortness of breath, pruritus, skin rash, dry mouth, bitter taste, excessive salivation, anorexia, euphoria, depression, slurred speech, confusion, restlessness, hallucinations, and elevated SGOT, SGPT, total and direct bilirubens, and alkaline phosphatase. Paradoxical reactions, e.g., excitement, stimulation and hyperactivity, have also been reported in rare instances.

The warnings speak for themselves. No William Jennings Bryan, no Clarence Darrow can deliver indictments more eloquent than those contained in the admonitions issued by the manufacturer itself. And bear in mind that to the manufacturer's own cautions must be added three more: possible dependence, possible lethal effects, and finally, the strongest condemnation of all, long-term effects unknown.

Our uneasiness reflects that of some of the most highly respected and responsible members of the medical profession. In 1977, a panel of experts which was convened by the National Institute on Drug Abuse to review current knowledge regarding the clinical use, effectiveness, and benefits of the sedative-hypnotic compounds registered considerable disagreement over the conclusiveness of evidence that *flurazepam* (**Dalmane**) is clinically superior to barbiturate hypnotics. An examination of the evaluations of this group of distinguished medical professors reveals their recognition of the possibility that the benzodiazepines may yet prove to be more toxic when administered chronically than even the malevolent barbiturates.

The information is in your hands. We should like to use, in this context, with a diametrically opposed injunction, the slogan of a well-known hypnotic-drug company. Now that you know what you must do, "THE REST IS EASY."

Prescripts and Proscripts for Medication

• As of June 1978, the active ingredients of OTC sleep preparations were not recognized as both safe and effective by the Commissioner of the Food and Drug Administration. Avoid all OTC sleep preparations.

• Almost all prescription sedative-hypnotics are effective for a few nights. In times of extreme stress or crisis, the use of a sleeping pill, with your doctor's approval, may furnish the comfort and rest you require for the emergency period. They should not be used beyond a few nights.

• All sleep preparations must be strictly avoided during pregnancy. The effect of medication upon the unborn baby is largely unknown. In most cases, controlled tests have not been conducted. The safety of **Dalmane** during pregnancy, for example, has not been established.

• If you are taking a sleep medication, under no circumstances should you take more than your doctor has recommended. If your pill no longer puts you to sleep, you have become habituated—you have developed a tolerance. You do yourself a disservice when you take two pills, or add a second pill with a different name. If you cannot sleep, try to roll with the punches. Remind yourself that you will sleep tomorrow night, or the next night, but do not risk a long-term case of drug dependency for the sake of the next few hours of sleep. Spend the rest of the night without sleep if necessary, remembering that sleeplessness will not injure your health in any way, and in the morning start a program to revise your sleep habits according to the prescripts and proscripts which apply to your habits and to your problems.

• If you are one of the hundreds of thousands of individuals who ingest drugs on a regular basis, the best time to stop is now. Immediately. This week. Many people tell us that they are waiting for a favorable time to stop taking pills. Postponement is an excuse. The most favorable time is now. The sooner you start your program, the sooner you will complete this urgent assignment. First, of course, you must consult your doctor. He will probably advise you to taper your dosage gradually. Most physicians recommend a decrease of one therapeutic dose each week.

Mark was taking **Doriden.** His prescription called for a strength of 500 mg. Of his own accord, he had gradually elevated his dose by taking first two, and then three pills, on most nights. His physician prescribed the following withdrawal schedule, to be followed strictly. No exceptions were permitted.

First week	Two 500 mg. tablets every night.
Second week	One 500 mg. tablet every night.
Third week	One 500 mg. tablet every second night.
Fourth week	One 500 mg. tablet every third night.
Fifth week	No medication.

Mark experienced discomfort during the first two weeks. He could not fall asleep for hours on most nights. He suffered stomach pains and nausea, but was not certain whether they were related to his reduction of medication. Exhausted, irritable, and depressed during the day, the quality of his work deteriorated. In retrospect, months later, he appreciated that the necessity to work while tapering had been helpful in taking his mind off his problems. After the first two weeks, he felt greatly improved. He still experienced prevailing depression, but he averaged approximately five hours of sleep each night. By week number five, he was ready to throw his pills away and to try to learn new sleep habits.

Ira's physician employed a different method. Ira had been using 100 mg. of *secobarbital* for many years. When he informed his physician that he wanted to release himself from the drug, the physician wrote a prescription for 50 mg. of *flurazepam* **(Dalmane).** Ira surrendered the *secobarbital* the very first night and started on **Dalmane.** Contrary to his expectations, he encountered few nightmares, although his nights were filled with troubled dreams and he slept restlessly at best. After three uncomfortable weeks on 50 mg., his dose was reduced to a weaker strength. He continued taking **Dalmane** for several months, unable to marshal the strength to give up the drug completely. Finally, one night, after three full months, he gathered the inner resource to undertake a final effort, and he began a scheduled progressive withdrawal. Ira has now discarded all sleep medication of any kind. Occasionally, when he feels impelled to take a pill, he swallows two aspirin tablets, and he reports that sleep, aware that no stronger enticement will be forthcoming, accepts with good grace the aspirin's illusory invitation.

• All of the evidence shows that sleep medicines offer no permanent advantage at all. Beyond a few days, or at most a few weeks, of regular use, the effect of the drug is lost completely. On a purely anecdotal level, without any controlled measurement, people have informed us that their pills allow them to fall asleep more quickly than they could fall asleep without the medication. Even if this impression is correct, and it may not be at all correct, it is surely a minor benefit to weigh against the host of damages which accompany the use of drugs. Among the disadvantages is one rarely mentioned, but insidiously malicious—that of bondage. Try to remember all of the petty rules your bondage to a drug imposes. How many times do you check to make certain you have your pill with you when you sleep away from home? How often do you remind yourself to renew your prescription? How often do you search your memory to recall whether you have taken your pill on any particular night? Do you ever feel sedated in the morning? Do you ever worry whether your pill will interact with wine at dinner, or with another medication? Over and above everything else we have already discussed, do you really need these disabling irritations to trouble you like a cluster of itching mosquito bites? Do not let the petty tryanny of the sleeping pill interfere with your spontaneity, with your serenity, with your health, and, most important of all, with your ability to sleep naturally. Make your decision today. Give up your pills tonight.

In summary:
• Avoid OTC sleep preparations.
• Scrupulously avoid all sleep preparations, both OTC and prescription drugs, during pregnancy.
• Never increase the dosage of a prescribed sleep medication.
• Limit the period during which you take prescribed sleep drugs to a few consecutive nights at most, even in times of crisis.
• If you presently use sleep drugs regularly, consult your doctor for a withdrawal schedule. It is wise to taper use of even supposedly innocuous preparations gradually.

CHAPTER 10

Food for Sleep

Gordon, a friend of ours, habitually fell asleep at dinner parties. Sometimes his eyes closed at the climax of a fascinating story, sometimes during a witty exchange. His heavy lids provided eloquent indication to the company in general, and to his hosts specifically, that the evening was a bore. A number of amateur raconteurs felt compelled to reevaluate their favorite stories in the face of Gordon's soporific reaction. Most embarrassed of all was his wife, who repeatedly threatened to cancel all dinner engagements, and then just as repeatedly relented on Gordon's promise to remain awake, a promise he consistently disregarded.

During the course of a routine medical examination, Gordon discovered that he was hypoglycemic. When he ate desserts and other carbohydrate foods, his system overreacted in an exaggerated version of the normal physiological response to carbohydrates. He was placed on a diet for hypoglycemia in order to alleviate symptoms unrelated to his habit of falling asleep at social gatherings. In a matter of weeks, Gordon stopped falling asleep after dinner.

Gordon's sleepiness and his prescribed diet suggest directives for your insomnia and for your diet. Drawing from an extension of experimental findings, with Gordon as an illustrative example in reverse, we are going to offer a prescript which has heretofore never been advanced, one which you will find extremely helpful and entirely palatable. You will find it more than palatable; you will find it delicious.

Before we make any recommendations, let us examine the natural chemicals which counteract insomnia. We will discuss only substances which are found in common foods, as opposed to drug compounds which are classified as sleep medications, and which are discussed separately in Chapter Nine.

Tryptophan, a food extract, is now on the market, but its properties have not as yet been subjected to long-term tests. Pending more definitive test results, an examination of the bio-chemistry of sleep will assist you to make your own informed decision regarding this new sleeping pill, tryptophan. Tryptophan, unlike sleep medications, is not a drug compound manufactured by a chemical company, but is rather an amino acid, a natural substance found in certain foods. Available in capsule or tablet form, it is generally sold in health food stores. We must emphasize that tryptophan is not a cure for insomnia. At best, it is an aid to better sleep.

Our average daily diets contain in natural form from one to two grams of tryptophan, combined with other food components. Tryptophan, in extract form, can be taken to augment your natural daily intake. It is important to appreciate that the tryptophan you obtain in your food does not behave in your body in exactly the same fashion as the tryptophan you ingest in extract form.

The end product of tryptophan is called *serotonin.* Serotonin is a body chemical intimately and critically involved in sleep. It is manufactured inside the body itself, and is found in selected areas of the brain. The serotonin production line is dependent upon the tryptophan which you ingest either in foods, or in pure extract form, or in both. Tryptophan is converted in your body to *L-tryptophan,* and thence by the action of an enzyme to *5-0 H-tryptophan,* and finally to serotonin. The tryptophan passes from the cells of your intestinal walls into the bloodstream, where, carried by the blood plasma, it circulates throughout your body and is subjected to various changes. Conversion from tryptophan to serotonin occurs inside the brain. Some experimenters have reasoned that serotonin may act in concert with other body chemicals in a complex orchestration of roles. But all agree that serotonin is a critical element for sleep.

The reports detailing the discovery of serotonin as an agent which induces sleep read like the painstaking pursuit of clues in an Edgar Allen Poe mystery story. First one line of reasoning was followed, and then another, until all converged upon serotonin. First, a chemical substance known to obstruct the manufacture of serotonin was injected into animals, and total insomnia resulted. Without serotonin, they could not sleep. When serotonin was reintroduced into these same animals, insomnia was reversed—the animals slept. These same results were obtained by means of surgical procedures. When the manufacture of serotonin was prevented, insomnia resulted. With excessive serotonin, hypersomnia, too much sleep, was produced.

All of these experiments performed upon animals point to serotonin as a critical element in sleep. Within the past fifteen years, studies of human subjects have supported the results obtained with animals. Humans who ingested tryptophan, which helps activate serotonin, gained a significant improvement in sleep.

Ernest Hartmann of Boston State Hospital has been investigating the effects of tryptophan on sleep since 1964. A series of studies which compared the sleep of human subjects after they had taken either L-tryptophan (a form of tryptophan) or a placebo, reported generally positive findings. Improved sleep with L-tryptophan was seen in psychiatric patients, in hospitalized alcoholics, and in normal men and women who suffered mild insomnia. All of these groups fell asleep more quickly with L-tryptophan than with a placebo. The studies revealed an increase in the total amount of sleep, and a decrease in waking time during the night, as well as in the early morning. In our Somniquest terminology, L-tryptophan was effective in the alleviation of initardia, pleisomnia, and, to a lesser extent, scurzomnia.

In his studies, Dr. Hartmann employed a "double-blind" technique, an interesting device which eliminates bias. Biased results are particularly strong in cases which involve medication. When an experimenter administers medication to a subject, a subtle form of involuntary communication occurs. Probably because of the experimenter's interest, experimental medication is dispensed with enthusiasm, while the placebo is offered mechanically. The attitude and the expectation of the experimenter is spelled out clearly, both verbally and by silent behavior, to the subject. In order to guard against the intrusion of this extraneous obstacle, a "blind" technique is employed. The experimenter who administers the medication is unaware whether the medication is the actual experimental substance, or whether it is the placebo. This combination, unaware experimenter plus unaware subject, is called a "double-blind" technique, and was utilized in the studies of tryptophan reported by Dr. Hartmann.

In some of the studies of human reactions to L-tryptophan, the dosage was varied from one gram to as high as seven grams. A comparison of results of ingesting the various dosages showed that one gram would produce the full effect, and there was no further improvement with higher doses. This finding is consistent with animal studies, which revealed that beyond a ceiling level no further increase in brain serotonin was produced by additional tryptophan. A second finding indicated that sleep patterns were not distorted by L-tryptophan, even when it was ingested for twenty-eight successive nights. You will recall that many hypnotic drugs interfere with dream sleep, and a dream rebound occurs when the drug is discontinued. Here, however, sleep patterns were unaffected by discontinuance of L-tryptophan, except for a continuing slight increase in deep sleep which persisted after the substance was halted.

Most important for health, Dr. Hartmann reports that L-tryptophan seems to be rapidly cleared from the body. It exerts its soporific effect most strongly early in the night, and is then discarded. Preliminary tests indicated that it is not habit-forming.

In short, L-tryptophan appears to be most promising as an aid to better sleep. It carries special appeal because it is a natural substance found in food rather than a chemical compound. But a note of uncertainty intrudes even as we consider the virtues of L-tryptophan in powder or tablet form. It is important to remember that a highly concentrated extract of tryptophan is not the same as tryptophan found in food, where it combines with other components. Tryptophan in isolation has already demonstrated a slightly different effect from tryptophan in food. While this effect has been salutary, until long-term testing has been completed one can merely speculate. Although the probability of safety seems good, a definite and positive conclusion as to other possible side effects cannot yet be reported. Additionally, every characteristic of an extract such as tryptophan must be fully investigated and checked, before continuous use can be recommended. Even the process by which the extract is obtained requires careful examination. In at least one instance, a therapeutic agent which was in itself beneficial was contaminated by substances utilized in its preparation. One natural health product company reports that L-tryptophan, the more readily absorbed form of tryptophan, is extracted from yeast and sold in capsule form. We do not know whether the process interferes with the final product, although we have no reason to believe that it does. Other companies may obtain tryptophan by other methods. Here again, we must await definitive answers before any final judgment can be formed.

Still another *caveat* relates to possible side effects. To date, only nausea has been reported, and this at doses considerably higher than the recommended one gram. Time and further testing may uncover no additional side effects, but any conclusions regarding their absence are at this time premature.

The decision remains in your hands. Tryptophan or L-tryptophan in powder, tablet, or capsule form appears to be safe as an occasional aid to sleep. It seems to carry many advantages over a sleep drug. For continuous use, an affirmative determination must be deferred.

Although you will not wish to take L-tryptophan tablets on a regular basis until long-term safety has been established, you should make certain to eat foods which are high in this substance in order to assist yourself in your quest for sleep. A balanced diet will furnish a base level of tryptophan. A list of foods high in tryptophan, which you may take in order to boost your daily intake, appears in the Appendix. For people who eat at normal times, tryptophan levels in the blood drop to a low at two to four o'clock in the morning, and then gradually rise to a plateau in the late afternoon. Though you may take foods high in tryptophan concentration at any time during the day, if you tend to fall asleep in the afternoon, you should reserve these foods for your evening meal, so that their effect will be greatest when you require it most, at bedtime.

A series of animal studies has yielded results which carry implications for brain serotonin, and thus for sleep, in humans. They may also help explain why our friend Gordon fell asleep after dinner. These studies, by extension, suggest a simple and pleasurable method of improving your sleep through food.

The experimenters manipulated various foods, or food constituents, and then measured serotonin. They found that, although tryptophan extract converted to serotonin readily, tryptophan in food was not utilized unless taken with carbohydrates or a carbohydrate-fat combination. In other words, carbohydrates and carbohydrate-fat combinations liberate tryptophan, so that it can do its job. This explains what was probably happening to Gordon. His intake of carbohydrates during the day and at dinner was high, and these carbohydrates increased the serotonin which contributed to Gordon's evening torpor. His new diet for hypoglycemia reduced the carbohydrates, and permitted Gordon to remain awake. Gordon's problem was staying awake. Your problem, of course, is getting to sleep. And so we are suggesting Gordon's prescription in reverse—we are urging that you eat carbohydrates, but, as indicated in our prescripts and proscripts, eat them at night.

While the investigators advise that there is, at the present time, no information concerning the effect of carbohydrates on brain tryptophan and serotonin in humans, we have undertaken to reason by extension from the animal studies. Human processes, while not identical, are similar to those of the lower animals, and an application of the findings in animal studies to human food ingestion suggests that a simple manipulation of your present dietary habits should be pursued to encourage the body chemical production of serotonin—the natural sleep elixir.

And now for the sweet prescript we promised.

Prescripts and Proscripts for Food for Sleep

It may seem too good to be true, but a chocolate bar can help you sleep. It can obviously also help you get fat, and there is no point in substituting one discomfort for another. We are not suggesting chocolate, or its equivalent, as an addition to your diet, but we are urging that you transfer some of your chocolate or carbohydrate intake away from your daytime routine and into your pre-bedtime schedule, where it can assist in your search for sleep.

• To state this prescript in general terms, you must eat a high-carbohydrate food before you go to bed for the night. Carbohydrates include sugars and starches in candies, cakes, and fruits. A fruit-fat combination is equally effective. These foods will neutralize amino acid competition and thus enable the brain to utilize tryptophan without hindrance, thereby producing serotonin and sleep. A list of high-carbohydrate foods and of fruit-fat combinations appears in the Appendix.

• In terms of your general food intake, you must make certain to eat a balanced diet which is high in tryptophan. A list of high-concentrate tryptophan foods appears on pages 206-207. In the natural course of events, body levels rise and fall cyclically without regard to minimal dietary variations during the day. Therefore, you may eat these foods at any time, but in order to boost tryptophan levels at night it is best to reserve them for your evening meal. If, for some reason, you do not eat your usual full quota of tryptophan foods on any given day, you need not worry about sleep on that account. The circadian cycle will continue to draw upon reserves to accomplish a rise and fall of tryptophan in the blood at various times of the day and night.

The average person consumes a total of one to two grams of food tryptophan in a daily diet. You will probably not be able to add an additional full gram of food tryptophan in your diet (the full effect of pure extract tryptophan is achieved with one gram), but you will surely be able to consume more tryptophan than is your custom now, and that should be your objective. Tryptophan quantities are listed in milligrams. One thousand milligrams equal one gram.

• With reference to the carbohydrate intake ordered in our first prescript, if your problem is initardia (inability to fall asleep when you get into bed) you should eat your high-carbohydrate food two to four hours before bed, so that the food will reach its peak effect when you are ready to retire.

If, on the other hand, your difficulty is either pleisomnia (frequent awakenings after you fall asleep), or scurzomnia (short sleep), or hyperlixia (light sleep), you should eat your high-carbohydrate food immediately before bed. Since falling asleep in the first instance is not your problem, you will want the carbohydrates to operate at top efficiency after you have been sleeping for a few hours, which is approximately when your sleep problem normally appears. In any event, you yourself are aware of your insomnia time schedule, and you can adjust your carbohydrate intake accordingly.

- If you tend to fall asleep during the day or early in the evening you must eliminate carbohydrates during the day. Eat these foods before bedtime only. With reference to falling asleep during the day, you will recall, of course, our repeated injunction that afternoon naps and dozing at any time before you get to bed should be avoided in all cases.

- In order to forestall a weight gain, your carbohydrate food should not be added to your usual diet, but instead it should be transferred from breakfast or lunch to the evening. If you are accustomed to dessert at your evening meal, you should defer your dessert until the time appropriate for your particular sleep problem, approximately two to four hours before bedtime for initardia, and at bedtime for the other insomnias, or any variation, depending on your own private sleep-problem timetable.

- In any case, it is crucial that you keep in mind the fact that we are advising carbohydrate intake only before your bedtime. Whatever you do, you must never succumb to Myron's banana habit, and eat chocolate, ice cream, or anything else if, after falling asleep, you awaken during the night.

In summary:
- Eat a balanced diet which is high in tryptophan.
- Eat a high-carbohydrate food or a carbohydrate-fat combination approximately two to four hours before your problem usually occurs.
- If your sleep problem arises in the early morning, eat your snack directly before retiring.
- Reduce or eliminate carbohydrate consumption during the day.
- Never eat anything during the night.

CHAPTER 11

Good Night

You are now ready to start your campaign against insomnia. You are familiar with the directives which you must follow. We trust that your decision to accept our prescripts and proscripts will remain firm and that your spirits will be high. At the start of your new sleep program, the danger of immediate defeat is minimal, given your strong motivation to train yourself into fresh sleep habits. Nor will your first few weeks prove critical. You will, during those early weeks, be struggling to overcome habits which hinder sleep, and if you are determined, you will surely prevail over any inclinations to repeat previous mistakes. Soon, you will begin to notice gains. For some, the gains will be large and steady. Others will take two steps forward and one step back before they forge ahead again. Occasionally a plateau is reached along the road to better sleep; improvement seems to stand still before the next spurt ahead.

As you grow accustomed to sleeping well, you will become complacent. As paradoxical as this may seem, your need for vigilance will reach its crisis stage during the period immediately following a clear improvement in the quality and the quantity of your sleep, a period when you begin to take better sleep for granted. This is the period when the phenomenon of spontaneous recovery will appear. Although all of us have encountered spontaneous recovery in our lives or in the lives of those who are close to us, most of us generally do not appreciate this phenomenon as an automatic, involuntary process. And yet it is so elementary a behavioral practice it may be observed in a goldfish, a guinea pig, or in any other laboratory animal.

In the laboratory, a hungry white rat is placed in a cage. Located on one side of the cage, an inch or two above the floor, is a small, rectangular metal bar. Whenever this bar is depressed, a pellet of food rolls down through a chute and into a cup inside the cage. The rat has not been trained. In the course of exploring the cage, at some point, quite by chance, the rat places his paw on the bar, whereupon the bar clicks and a pellet drops into the cup. The rat seizes and devours the tiny ball. After two or three such sessions in the cage, the rat acquires the bar-press habit. Thereafter, the habit becomes so strong that each succeeding time the rat is placed in the cage, he runs directly to the bar, and he presses and eats, presses and eats, until his hunger is satisfied.

And now, after this behavior pattern is firmly established, the experimenter undertakes to break the bar-press habit. Extinction is simple. It is only necessary to eliminate the pellets of food. The rat will continue to press the bar for a few frustrating sessions, during which the pellets do not roll into the cup, and then the bar-press behavior is finally discontinued. If, then, the experimenter continues to place the hungry rat inside the cage day after day, the animal will ignore the bar. The habit has been broken. It is extinguished. But now the rat is about to reach the crisis. If the experimenter goes beyond the habit-breaking point and persists in placing the hungry rat inside the cage, before long a strange behavior will be observed. One day, abruptly, this same rat will march directly to the bar and will press it repeatedly, just as if extinction had never occurred. The old habit has been reinvigorated by a process known to behavioral scientists as *spontaneous recovery*.

You are familiar with spontaneous recovery. You have encountered friends or acquaintances who have stopped smoking for a substantial period of time, only to start all over again after the habit was defeated. Spontaneous recovery of former habit strength accomplished the regression. You know men and women who have lost substantial weight by dieting. They look refreshed. They tell you how much better they feel. They buy new clothes.

They are complimented repeatedly. Their old eating habits have disappeared, they are no longer hungry in mid-afternoon. They tell you, proudly, that the desire for a cheeseburger with french fried potatoes has vanished. And then, inexplicably, one day at lunch your friend orders the cheeseburger and the french fried potatoes, and more than that, stops to buy a chocolate bar on the way back to the office. Before long, you observe all of the lost weight reappear. Spontaneous recovery of former habit strength is once again the culprit. Have you ever experienced an unhappy love affair? Do you remember the yearning, the longing, the ache inside yourself? Do you also remember how the yearning slowly lost its intensity? Do you recall your relief when the pain went away? And then, later, did a voice, a scent, a place, a memory suddenly revive the former ache in all of its excruciating force? That revival represented spontaneous recovery.

Our warning to you now is a warning against spontaneous recovery. You are about to embark upon a new sleep course. If you have discovered that your inability to sleep is related to your sleep habits, and you have learned which of those habits must be eliminated, you know now the procedures which you must pursue. If you succeed in winning your fight against insomnia, you will sleep more restfully, and within a short period of time you will feel more relaxed about sleep. But then the strong drive which propelled you during your struggle will ebb away. You will be left defenseless. It is then, when your defenses are down, that the automatic resurgence of habit strength, spontaneous recovery, will appear. And so you must never diminish your vigilance. You must not, having won the battle, lose the war. You must never return to the habits which fostered your insomnia.

It is unfortunately true that during the period of spontaneous recovery you will experience discomfort, just as the erstwhile dieter feels uncomfortable in response to a demand which his body presents insistently once more. The laboratory animal pressing the bar after its habit has been extinguished bears down forcefully and rapidly, emphasizing its frustration. But if the experimenter continues to deny food during the spontaneous recovery interval, the bar-press behavior stops quickly, and in most cases permanently. There is a lesson to be learned from all of this. You must not permit yourself to fail on the brink of success. You must be careful to avoid the type of behavior exhibited by proverbial dieters who, losing thousands of pounds, manage to remain obese. Your new regimens, geared to your specific problems, must be scrupulously followed always and forever. If you can change your sleep habits in the first instance, and if then you can prevent a regression during spontaneous recovery, you will gain the permanent reward of restful sleep.

As a therapist, as your own therapist, you will wish to determine the prognosis for your patient, yourself. The prospect of change rests in a delicate balance. The competing forces must be weighed on a set of scales, like the scales of justice. On one side of the scale on a brass tray sits the persistent habit, in full strength. On the other tray, also in full strength, lies your motivation, your determination to break the habit. Obviously, determination strength must weigh heavier than habit strength before the scale will tip for sleep.

Before you reach your prognosis, you must, with total objectivity, weigh *your* patient's motivation. If you as your therapist can recognize in yourself as your patient a genuine and unequivocal desire to change, an absolute need to sleep undisturbed and without interruption, then your recognition of your own bona fide interest would justify an expectation of favorable results. You should, however, bear in mind how many dieters will enthusiastically pledge a schedule of semistarvation a few hours before ordering a chocolate-nut-fudge sundae. Hundreds of thousands of heavy smokers swear equally resolute vows in the middle of the night while wracked with spasms of coughing. What happens to the smoker's resolution in the morning, after a cup of coffee? What will happen to your resolution when you are faced with a choice between an old but comfortable habit, and a new and inconvenient prescript?

Your motivation may be weakened if your particular prescripts and proscripts instruct you to sleep less when you are yearning to sleep more. It must seem cruel to you to be told to reach your goal by traveling in the opposite direction. It is not easy to go west when you wish to reach east. The ability to take a circuitous route, which is actually your assignment, requires a good measure of abstract intelligence. Experiments have shown that a lower animal, a chicken, will starve to death while looking at food on the other side of an open-ended fence. A more intelligent animal, a dog, will survey the situation and will then dash around the open end of the fence, heading left in order to reach its destination straight ahead. And for the thousands of years that man has been sailing the seas he has employed the same device. If the sailor's port is north, and the wind blows south, even the apprentice seaman will tack, zigging west, then zagging east, in order to reach north. And so with you. Like the seaman, you must tack.

While you assess your own drive for better sleep, you must prepare yourself against yet another possible obstacle which may undermine your motivation. You must arm yourself against the operations of a secret agent known as *secondary gain*. Secondary gain refers to the surreptitious comfort we extract from even the most unpleasant situations. Strange as it may seem, even the most serious of disabilities will generally confer incidental benefits upon the victim. For example, a bedridden patient is relieved of responsibilities, an immediate gain. When, as sometimes happens, secondary gain gathers a sufficient number of benefits, it operates to maintain the disability from which it stems. We treated Doris, a woman who was incapacitated by a neuromuscular disorder. When the topic of secondary gain was introduced, Doris, along with other members of the group, was astonished by the suggestion that insomnia could produce any advantages whatsoever. And yet her husband hurried home from his office every Wednesday evening to drive her to our meeting, showing the kind of solicitude all of us would surely welcome. When Doris slept, her daughter would pass the uncarpeted floor outside her mother's bedroom on tiptoe, and each time Doris heard the light footsteps, she received renewed assurance of her daughter's devotion. The entire family spoke in whispers whenever Doris napped. Even her friends concentrated on her sleep problem. Doris herself considerately refused to burden her friends with any detail of her serious illness, and they in turn lavished all of their attention upon her insomnia, a topic which allowed them to express their affection. In view of these aspects of Doris's insomnia, you can appreciate that her inability to sleep conferred, along with its discomfort, a considerable number of fringe benefits.

The ill wind of insomnia blows some good by way of attention, concern, and displays of love which the insomniac, like all of us, cherishes dearly. But when these secondary gains accumulate a sufficient degree of force, they operate to maintain the insomnia habit. They also undermine the urge to root out and to extinguish the behavior which maintains poor sleep. An assessment of your own store of secondary gain will require cool objectivity. It will not be easy for you to take inventory, but it is essential that you do so. Take careful note of each escape from obligation, each release from responsibility, and each expression of devotion which you receive as a result of your insomnia. Your mere awareness, your own acknowledgment of your secondary gain, will, by itself, help to counteract the impact. If you can take one further step, if you can bring yourself to surrender your secondary gain entirely, you will defeat your own contrary tendencies. When you are asked how you slept, could you possibly respond with a noncommittal answer, and then quickly change the subject? Could you forgo all other gains? Think of your renunciations as an investment. In place of the solicitude of your children or your spouse, you will help yourself to better sleep. In exchange for breakfast in bed, or some other such luxury, a store of early-morning energy awaits you. The investment is large, but the return is high.

Processes other than secondary gain may also sap the strength of motivation. Rationalization is such a process. Celia, vice-president of a bank, is a crisp, efficient woman. When she registered for our course, she suffered deep distress because of her inability to sleep. Celia was a victim of initardia and hyperlixia. She believed that she also suffered scurzomnia, but inasmuch as she spent eight hours in bed, her actual sleep time was undetermined. This much was clear: Celia was chronically tired and worn as a result of poor sleep, and her entire daytime activities were affected by her inability to rest. She did display energy, but it was nervous energy—it lacked buoyancy. She performed her daily chores with more somber determination than zest.

Celia found it difficult to follow instructions. Her greatest obstacle was the prescript which directed her to go to bed later in the evening, to rise from bed earlier in the morning, and to leave her bed at night whenever she was awake. Several weeks passed before she could bring herself to take her first step, and then finally her sleep did improve, but only slightly the first week of her new routine. Celia was disappointed that she did not achieve a one-hundred-percent cure immediately, a disappointment which is common to those who try to break a long-standing habit. It was spring. Her daughter and her son-in-law, a medical student in Chicago, visited Celia during the school spring recess. When we next saw Celia after her daughter's visit, she had changed. She assumed a new, detached, and somewhat distant attitude. She informed us that her son-in-law, the young doctor, believed in the quality of spontaneity as an ultimate value. He was opposed to schedules, to routines, to rules of any kind. Celia ought to go to bed, stay in bed, eat in bed, when and as the spirit moved her. We too appreciate spontaneity. We can understand that spontaneity is generally a desirable attribute, but spontaneity in every case is nonsense. Would anyone advise an alcoholic to drink liquor spontaneously? Could any serious student of medicine urge a diabetic to indulge in a chocolate mousse spontaneously? What about sauerkraut, pastrami, salted cod? For those who suffer hypertension, spontaneity with those foods could prove destructive. The medical student's error reflected a common misconception, a failure to perceive that insomnia, like alcoholism and overeating, is a pernicious habit which can be eliminated only by careful retraining.

Nevertheless, Celia opted for spontaneity.

Celia's desire to sleep comfortably was strong, but unfortunately her urge to change her habits was weak. And so she employed a popular defense mechanism: rationalization. Celia rationalized by accepting her son-in-law's advice: behave spontaneously. The rationalization mechanism permits us to indulge our desires with freedom, because it justifies the indulgence. When we rationalize, we find a logical reason to do exactly as we wish. A little girl we knew habitually spent her entire weekly allowance on the same day she received it from her mother. The moment the money was placed in her eager little hand, she was seized with a desire to spend every penny. Each week, her mother patiently lectured the child, who genuinely wished to save her money as instructed, but who was unable to control her compulsion to spend. One Friday afternoon, the child's "pay day," she listened solemnly to her mother's stricture, and then hurried directly to a neighborhood store. She returned within half an hour to display proudly to her mother the toy bank which she had purchased with her entire allowance, explaining, in a classical illustration of rationalization, that she simply had to have a bank in which to place her savings.

We have all discovered logical reasons to indulge our preferences. Like Celia, you will find, if you search even briefly, any number of justifications for pursuing habits which support insomnia. However, if your desire to change is strong enough, you will not succumb. We offer you one consideration to overcome any argument that the process of rationalization may suggest. That consideration is better sleep.

Karl dozed lightly and intermittently during our meetings. He was an overweight man who spoke with a strong German accent. He breathed heavily. His poor sleep had flared up many years earlier, when he was discharged from the army. He followed strict, rigid routines. He walked each day a distance of one and one-tenth miles, to the Long Island Railroad station to catch the 7:31 to Brooklyn. He returned on the 5:17, and he regularly fell asleep on the return trip. Sundays were spent with his family, Saturdays with his wife's family. His habits were firm, his loyalties were strong. He was particularly attached to his family doctor, a practitioner who had treated Karl for more than twenty years. We were convinced, and we remain convinced, that an examination in a sleep laboratory was indicated to determine whether Karl was a victim of sleep apnea. He received our advice gravely, and returned the following week, smiling with relief. His doctor had laughed outright at the notion of any sleep disorder, scoffing, reassuring Karl, and mechanically renewing Karl's prescription for *Valium.* Karl left the doctor with a sense of satisfaction—temporarily. The last time we saw Karl, he was breathing heavily, and from time to time his eyelids would close as he tried to snatch a few moments of precious sleep.

Celia and Karl, along with Thelma discussed earlier, all failed. We could not reach them. All of us are free to rationalize, like Celia, or to shop around for an opinion which coincides with our wishes, like Karl. However, there is a price which must be paid. Celia and Karl's choice to satisfy their immediate impulses left both of them with the same discomfort which had impelled them to seek assistance in the first place.

In contrast to Celia and Karl, Theresa, who suffered no sleep problem discovered, oddly enough, that Somniquest could be helpful in areas unrelated to sleep. Theresa is an occupational therapist at a metropolitan hospital. She is employed in the psychiatric ward, and her patients often complained to her of sleep problems. Theresa did not know how to help them. The hospital's medical staff offered nothing more than pills. With special concern for one particular patient who suffered repeated nightmares, Theresa registered for the Somniquest program, and took careful note of our explanations of insomnia turbula, together with our suggestions for overcoming bad dreams. Then, at the ward, she instructed her patient to wake himself up at the onset of a nightmare. To Theresa's delight, the patient improved. The entire ward was suffused with enthusiasm. An electrifying concept had been introduced. Each of us possesses a large measure of control over our own thoughts, not only while awake, but also while asleep. The concept was as exciting to Theresa as to the patients. She contemplated her own controls, her own storehouse of influence, her private vault from which she could draw on demand. She cast about for opportunities to test herself. Because sleep was not a problem to her, Theresa searched in other areas.

Ever since childhood, Theresa had been overcome by depression on Sunday evenings. Originally, during her school years, the depression was activated by weekend homework, which she invariably postponed until Sunday night, and by the prospect of certain distasteful Monday morning classes. But that was the past. Now, with no classes, no homework, and with a career she found gratifying, she could not understand why her Sunday evening depression should persist. Theresa decided to test her own behavior controls and their ability to dispel her depression. On the first Sunday morning of the test, she reviewed the chores which awaited her in the early evening. It was Theresa's custom, every Sunday evening, to prepare a shopping list for the following week, to sort the laundry for the washing machine, and then to manicure her fingernails while she watched television. On this particular Sunday Theresa decided to change her routine. She completed all of the assignments in the morning. Then, at night, her mind free of the pressure of the tasks, she discovered that she could watch her favorite television programs without depression. Theresa told us of her first success, and we noted that her experiment, however successful, compounded several variables. She had altered a number of conditions simultaneously, and therefore she could not be certain which change had dispelled her depression. First, she had decided, in a manifestation of will, that she was not going to feel depressed, and then, in addition to that initial determination, she had proceeded to eliminate several possible sources of despondence. There is no profit in quarreling with success, but nevertheless further tests would be required before any final evaluation could be formulated.

Shortly thereafter, Theresa was asked to speak during the Grand Rounds at her hospital. The hospital, a large metropolitan institution, is a teaching facility attached to a medical school. The interns and residents are selected from among the brightest, most capable applicants in the country. The senior staff is distinguished. As for the Grand Rounds, this is the term for a ceremonial teaching procedure. Periodically, interns and residents accompany selected members of the senior staff as they make their rounds. The group moves from patient to patient, as the specialists explain the intricate details of each case. Theresa had been selected to explain the therapies she designed for her patients as the group passed through the ward under her charge. The opportunity to speak was an honor, but it was also threatening.

For three days Theresa was engulfed in fright. Then, remembering her first successful experience with her Sunday night depression, she decided that she herself was in control and that she must therefore exercise her own restraints. She reflected that the anxiety need not intimidate her, that she could, if she exercised sufficient effort, banish her stage fright. She was not entirely certain that she could gather the reserves to steady a trembling voice, to forestall a gasp for breath, to answer an unexpected question. But she was determined to try. She prepared the material for her presentation carefully. Each time she rehearsed her part in the forthcoming discussion, she explained to herself that she was not frightened. With this self-imposed and resolute decision, with nothing more than naked resolution, her agitation subsided. On the day of the Rounds, Theresa felt stimulated and refreshed. The group proceeded slowly through the various wards scheduled for the day. The chief of psychiatry spoke first, explaining the concept of a total therapeutic milieu and the manner in which that concept applied to each of the patients. When, finally, Theresa addressed the group, she turned to face them calmly. The chief psychiatrist, a man in his sixties and the author of several books, was listening attentively. The director of nursing looked up at Theresa expectantly. One of the residents, a frequent luncheon companion, smiled conspiratorially in encouragement. As for

Theresa, her heart pounded in four separate, distinct booms, like the portentous beat of a military drum. She waited for one protracted moment for her heart to quiet, and then, with utter calm and complete self-possession, Theresa started to speak.

Her presentation was a triumph. She had conquered her fear. After the compliments the following day, the acknowledging nods of respect, after she had grown accustomed to her newly discovered talent as a speaker, Theresa took stock of her accomplishment. She had extended her sphere of influence from her external world to her own internal world. She sighed with satisfaction, and searched within herself for new regions to conquer.

Theresa was taking advantage of a generalization of effect, a phenomenon which will also serve you once you have successfully utilized your own influence over yourself. The same phenomenon was observed in another area by Lewis Terman, an investigator who pursued a large-scale study of genius, starting back in the 1930s and continuing for many years. Before Terman's study, it was widely believed that intellectual prodigies suffered all manner of defects in mental health, in personality, in physical constitution, and in general adjustment to life. Terman selected young people with high I.Q.s, and obtained data from each of them periodically through the years. His statistics revealed that these young men and women, far from suffering defects, actually excelled in all areas. They were not only superior intellectually, they were better athletes, they were more attractive in appearance, they were more popular with their peers, their marriages were more successful, they excelled in their vocations, they were, in short, preeminent in all regions of endeavor. These gifted youngsters were favored by a generalization of effect. One positive attribute imparted to them the self-confidence which enabled them to excel in another sphere, and another, and yet another.

You can take advantage of the same generalization of effect as soon as you first demonstrate your own powers. You need only to observe faithfully the prescripts and the proscripts which pertain to your particular problem. Even as with the prodigies, your own first self-conquest will open the door to another and then another in a series which will lead inevitably to happier nights—and happier days.

CHAPTER 12

Manual for Sleep

This is the manual with which you will work to retrain yourself to sleep. It contains the specific information and instructions that you will require in your personal sleep program. In this section, we repeat the prescripts and proscripts in their summarized, capsule form, so that they will be available for ready reference. They are arranged in the same order as the chapters. You may find it helpful to mark those items that apply specifically to you so that you can find them at a glance.

The Back-to-Bed Guide is supplied to assist you if you experience difficulty in determining when you should return to bed after a sleepless period. Many people have never monitored their own sensations as sleepiness intensifies and alertness diminishes. They cannot pinpoint when they are ready to sleep. The guide is designed as an aid in the choice of an optimal state. Only a few references to the guide will be necessary before you learn to recognize your own state of readiness.

Seven Somniant Techniques are explained and described. General instructions for their use are presented immediately preceding the first technique, on page 193. Make certain to give each of the techniques a trial before you choose the one that is most effective for you.

Prescripts and Proscripts Summarized

For Restful Sleep:
- Do nothing in bed but sleep.
- After thirty minutes of wakefulness, get out of bed.
- When you get out of bed during the night, do something that you find boring.
- Return to bed only when you feel sleepy.
- Do not eat, drink, or engage in other pleasurable activities during nighttime awakenings.
- Keep a warm body, a cool bedroom.
- Sexual activity is excepted from all blanket prohibitions. Sex is recommended as a general soporific.
- Practice a Somniant Technique (pp. 193-204) immediately upon retiring, or immediately after awakening during the night.

Initardia
- Keep a written record of the time it takes you to fall asleep.
- Set your morning alarm back one hour earlier and get out of bed immediately when it rings. Follow this procedure for seven days.
- Do not change your bedtime.
- On the seventh evening, set your alarm back one additional hour.
- On the next evening, go to bed one hour earlier than formerly.
- You may feel fatigue during the rollback. Do not give up. Maintain your schedule.
- If necessary, repeat the rollback after an interim period of two weeks.
- After you find yourself falling asleep more promptly, you may begin to lengthen your sleep span. Add fifteen minutes in bed either in the morning or at night for one entire week. Add no more than fifteen minutes.
- Repeat the fifteen-minute addition for another entire week, and then again, until you have restored one hour.
- If at any time you again experience difficulty in falling asleep, eliminate the last additional fifteen minutes and maintain your sleep span at the previous length.
- Develop a presleep ritual.

- Practice a Somniant Technique.
- Institute an exercise program.

Scurzomnia

- Exercise vigorously every day, preferably before 4:00 P.M.
- Delay your bedtime for one hour.
- Practice a Somniant Technique upon awakening during the night.
- Do not remain in bed awake for more than thirty minutes.
- When you get out of bed in the early morning, start your day immediately. However, remember to delay breakfast to a normal breakfast hour.
- Do not nap.

Hyperlixia

- Eliminate all daytime naps, catnaps, as well as full-fledged naps.
- Use conversation, puzzles, letter writing, and other strategies of your own choice to circumvent sleep during the day.
- When you awaken during the night, leave your bed after thirty minutes.
- If you cannot manage to leave your bed, look at your clock every ten minutes.
- If, in the process of tracking the passage of time, you fail to note a block of time, you must repeat silently, "I have been asleep." Continue this self-education process on subsequent nights.
- Engage in a regular program of vigorous activity.
- Limit liquids after 6:00 P.M.

Pleisomnia

- Do not remain in bed awake for more than thirty minutes.
- Return to bed only when you feel ready to sleep.
- Retire at your usual time.
- Set your alarm for one hour earlier than its present setting and get out of bed promptly when it rings.
- If, after one week, you do not experience marked improvement, subtract an additional half hour.
- When you find yourself awakening less frequently, you may restore your lost sleep time by moving your alarm ahead fifteen minutes each week.
- Start a program of vigorous exercise and follow it regularly.

- Think about pleasant dreams every night.
- Try to recall your dreams in the morning.
- Discharge anger in brief but forceful activity.

Insomnia Turbula
- Do not eat, drink, telephone, watch television, etc., in bed.
- Do not eat or drink anything except water during the night. Alcohol must be scrupulously avoided.
- Do not take prescribed sleep medication for more than ten consecutive days.
- Never increase the prescribed dosage of a drug.
- If you occasionally nap during the day, go to bed later than usual that night.
- Tire yourself with physical activity.
- Study the prologues to your nightmares or unpleasant dreams.
- Alert yourself to awaken as soon as a bad dream or nightmare begins.
- For the first two weeks of your program, when you awaken from an aborted nightmare, leave your bed. Sit in a chair for five minutes. During these five minutes, briefly stroke your right forearm with the fingertips of your left hand.
- After the initial two-week period, when you awaken from an aborted nightmare, you may remain in bed, but spend a few minutes awake stroking your forearm before you allow yourself to sink back into sleep.

Fear of Death
- Use perfumes and lotions, and wear nightclothes which will help you to look and feel attractive in bed.
- Engage in sexual activity as often as possible.
- Change your sleep environment.
- Give yourself a little extra luxury at bedtime.
- Describe to another person the heightened activity which occurs during the course of sleep.

Food for Sleep
- Eat a balanced diet which is high in tryptophan.
- Eat a high-carbohydrate food or a carbohydrate-fat combination approximately two hours before your problem usually occurs.

- If your sleep problem arises in the early morning, eat your snack directly before retiring.
- Reduce or eliminate carbohydrate consumption during the day.
- Never eat anything during the night.

Back-to-Bed Guide

In order to determine whether you are ready to fall asleep after leaving your bed, choose which column below best describes your condition.

A	B	C
animated	quiet	dreamy
stimulated	inactive	languid
lively	relaxed	sleepy
stirred up	calm	heavy-eyed
wide awake	serene	nodding
alert	placid	
awake	tranquil	
restless		

If you have chosen a descriptive term in column A, stay out of bed. If your state is described in column B, wait a little longer. If your condition appears in column C, you are ready to go back to bed.

Somniant Techniques

The following presleep exercises have been carefully developed and designed to help you fall asleep or return to sleep when you awaken at night. In order to decide which of the techniques works best for you, practice them one at a time in sequence, each every night for one full week.

Start with *The Sleep Swing.* Practice *The Sleep Swing* for seven consecutive nights. At the beginning of the second week, learn *The Sleep Stretch* and practice that technique for seven consecutive nights. Continue in this fashion until you have mastered all of the techniques. At the end of seven weeks, you should be sleeping better. Having now given each of them an adequate trial, you will be able to judge which is best for you in the event that a sleepless episode occurs in the future.

For best results precede the Somniant Technique of your choice with *The Sleep Stretch* every night.

The Sleep Swing

This Somniant Technique is designed to flood the neural channels with soothing material in such a way as to block the entrance of disturbing thoughts or unpleasant emotions. Your brain can accommodate a limited number of messages, just as a switchboard can accept a limited number of telephone lines. When all the lines are busy, no further calls can get through. The same principle explains current methods of natural childbirth, as well as procedures now in development for control of intractable pain. The simple technique explained below engages the right and left hemispheres, as well as the association areas, of the brain, plus the lower centers of the autonomic nervous system with the object of keeping out intrusive, sleep-disturbing thoughts. Practice this exercise until you are familiar with it.

1. Begin with slow, rhythmic monotonous counting. Thus:
    Sleep . . . Two . . . Three . . . Four . . .
    Sleep . . . Two . . . Three . . . Four . . .
    Sleep . . . Two . . . Three . . . Four . . .
    Do not read any further. Close your eyes and rehearse counting several times. Check back. Are you saying the correct sequence in a slow, steady rhythm? Repeat it silently. Proceed.

2. Think of yourself as a child. You are in a grassy field on a summer day. The sun is shining. There is a breeze. You are sitting on a swing which hangs from a tree. Visualize yourself swinging back and forth, slowly and rhythmically. Thus:
    Back . . . Forth . . . Back . . . Forth . . .
    Back . . . Forth . . . Back . . . Forth . . .
    Back . . . Forth . . . Back . . . Forth . . .
    You must see the swing exactly as described. Do not change the direction. Be sure to start with the back motion.

Now swing and count in unison. Thus:
Sleep ... Two ... Three ... Four ...
Back ... Forth ... Back ... Forth ...
Do not read any further. Practice counting while you visualize swinging until you can do it smoothly and automatically. Proceed.

3. Concentrate on breathing. Breathe slowly and deeply. Thus:
Inhale ... Exhale ... Inhale ... Exhale ...
Inhale ... Exhale ... Inhale ... Exhale ...
Inhale ... Exhale ... Inhale ... Exhale ...

4. Now synchronize counting, swinging, and breathing— performing them simultaneously. Thus:

Count silently:	Sleep ... Two ... Three ... Four ...
Visualize:	Back ... Forth ... Back ... Forth ...
Breathe:	Inhale ... Exhale ... Inhale ... Exhale

The Sleep Swing is performed while lying in bed in a comfortable position, with eyes closed. If unwelcome thoughts intrude occasionally, brush them away and continue the technique. It should be repeated for three or four minutes upon getting into bed or upon awakening during the night. You may find yourself falling asleep during the first few minutes. Occasionally, sleep occurs immediately after *The Sleep Swing* is discontinued.

The Sleep Stretch

In 1938, a relaxation technique was published by Dr. E. Jacobson. A few of our participants claimed that the technique is an ancient yoga exercise. In recent years, the method has been used for a wide variety of purposes.

We have adapted Dr. Jacobson's method so that the second part is performed while lying in bed. Other changes were introduced on the advice of Somniquest participants who, after testing several variations of *The Sleep Stretch*, were impressed with the effectiveness of the final version. The method was particularly appreciated by elderly or inactive people, who enjoyed the mild exercise of their muscles.

The Sleep Stretch is primarily a relaxation technique. In order to ascertain whether a muscle is relaxed, an antagonistic condition is first produced. Originally, the antagonistic condition was tension. We found tension to be unpleasant, so we substituted the stretch instead. The stretch is used as a reference point, as a standard of comparison by which you may judge the extent of the relaxation which follows.

Sit on the edge of your bed with your feet on the floor and your arms in a relaxed position at your sides. You are going to proceed from your head to your toes, stretching and then relaxing small segments of your body one at a time. Each time you stretch, the stretch position will be held for a count of four. This instruction will be indicated by the word "hold." When you see the instruction to hold, it will mean hold the stretch while you count slowly to four.

Face

Raise your eyebrows. Hold. Relax.

Shut your eyes tight. Hold. Open. Relax.

Purse your lips, thrusting them forward as far as you can. Hold. Relax.

With your lips together, stretch your mouth in a wide smile. Hold. Relax.

Drop your chin by opening your mouth. Allow your jaw to hang loose. Hold. Relax.

Neck

Stretch your neck straight up toward the ceiling. Hold. Relax.

Point your chin toward the ceiling. Hold. Relax.

Try to touch your right shoulder with your right ear. Only your head should move. The shoulder remains in place. Hold. Relax.

Repeat with left shoulder. Hold. Relax.

Drop your chin loosely to your chest. Move your chin to the right and then to the left in a swinging pendulum motion. Repeat three times for a total of four. Relax.

Arms

Bend your right arm so that your elbow points to the floor and your hand points to the ceiling. Press hard. Hold. Relax.

Repeat with left arm. Hold. Relax.

Try to touch your elbows together behind your back. Hold. Relax.

Stretch your right arm forward parallel to the floor. Stretch hard. Hold. Relax. Return your arm to your side.

Repeat with left arm. Hold. Relax. Return your arm to your side.

Wrists

With your right arm stretched out in front of you and parallel to the floor, bend your wrist up so that your fingers point to the ceiling. Hold. Relax. Return your arm to your side.

Repeat with left wrist. Hold. Relax. Return your arm to your side.

Now with your right arm stretched forward parallel to the floor, bend your wrist down so that your fingers point to the floor. Hold. Relax. Return your arm to your side.

Repeat with left wrist. Hold. Relax. Return your arm to your side.

Fist

Clench your right hand in a fist. Hold. Relax.

Repeat with left fist. Hold. Relax.

Fingers

Spread the fingers of your right hand as wide as you can. Hold. Relax.

Repeat with fingers of your left hand. Hold. Relax.

Upper Torso

Raise your right shoulder toward your right ear. Keep your head motionless. Hold. Relax.

Repeat with left shoulder. Hold. Relax.

Repeat once more, this time with both shoulders raised simultaneously. Hold. Relax.

Stretch your shoulders forward and toward each other. Hold. Relax.

Now lie on your bed on your back, with your head on your pillow, your legs stretched out, and your arms relaxed at your sides.

Lower Torso

Arch your back while you stretch your chest and abdomen upward as high as you can. Hold. Relax.

Tighten your abdomen by pulling the muscles inward as hard as you can. Hold. Relax.

Tighten the muscles of your buttocks. Hold. Relax.

Legs

Lift your right leg from the hip, keeping your knee straight. Hold. Relax.

Repeat with left leg. Hold. Relax.

Bend your right knee and pull your upper leg up and back to your abdomen. Hold. Relax. Return your leg to the stretched-out position on the bed.

Repeat with left leg. Hold. Relax. Return your leg to the stretched-out position.

Now bend your right knee so that it points to the ceiling, while the sole of your foot remains flat on the bed. Pull your right heel as close to your buttock as you can. Hold. Relax. Return your leg to the stretched-out position.

Repeat with left leg. Hold. Relax. Return your leg to the stretched-out position.

Feet

Start with your legs stretched out straight. Bend your right ankle back so that your toes point toward your head. Hold. Relax.

Repeat with left ankle. Hold. Relax.

Now stretch your right foot forward so that your toes point to the foot of the bed. Hold. Relax.

Repeat with left foot. Hold. Relax.

Toes

Spread the toes of your right foot apart as wide as you can. Hold. Relax.

Repeat with left foot. Hold. Relax.

Bend the toes, just the toes, of your right foot forward. Hold. Relax.

Repeat with the toes of your left foot. Hold. Relax.

Your entire body should now be relaxed.

After you have memorized the succession of body parts, perform each stretch-relax instruction three times, instead of once, before you move to the next set of muscles. You will find that you are stretching tension out of each segment of your body from your head down to your toes.

Windows on the World

You are going to imitate one of the natural precursors of sleep, a small muscular event which occurs as you sink into sleep. Whenever you fall asleep, a number of physical activities take place at approximately the same time: muscles relax, breathing becomes regular, blood pressure lowers, heart rate slows, and the eyes roll loosely in their sockets. The present Somniant Technique is designed to mimic the muscular orientation of the eyes in their upward orientation as they roll, and thereby to recruit the other concomitant behaviors, including the goal response of sleep.

The recruitment process is seen physiologically in the operation of reverberatory circuits on the cortex of the brain. A single neural impulse running around a circular chain soon excites adjacent pathways so that they, too, burst into activity. On another level, you have undoubtedly observed the recruitment process when you tried to retrieve an old memory. Think back to a time when an almost-forgotten song began to haunt you, a recurrent experience for all of us. Did a fragment of the melody insinuate itself into your thoughts, running around and around in tantalizing circles? You began to hum the tune, didn't you? After a while, the repetition of the melody recruited a phrase of the lyric. Then the phrase and the melody circled together, and as they did an entire line was recruited. It was called to mind. Then, quickly, the complete song was recalled, and, with it, the events, the people, the emotions connected with the song. In the manner of the reverberatory circuit and of the retrieval of an elusive memory, *Windows on the World* utilizes a recruitment process. It is particularly effective in lulling you back to sleep when you awaken at night.

Lie in bed in a comfortable position. You are going to approximate the upward turn of the eyes, as if you were moving from a relaxed presleep state into Stage 1 sleep. With your eyes closed, imagine that you have entered the elevator at Windows on the World, the restaurant located on the one hundred and seventh floor of one of the tallest buildings in the world. The elevator is about to descend. The door closes. With your mind's eye, look up at the indicator above the elevator door. The indicator will register each floor as it passes. The elevator moves down slowly, very slowly, from floor to floor. Imagine you feel the descent in your body as the elevator goes down.

107
106
105
104

Do not lower your eyes. The upward orientation of your eyes as you watch the imaginary indicator is the critical element. Continue watching as the elevator descends all the way to the first floor.

103
102
101
100
99
98
97
96
--
--
--

As you become sleepy, you may miscount. Go back to your mistake and continue the descent as before. Don't forget that the elevator is descending slowly. Most people fall asleep before they reach the lobby.

Sleep Vibes

Sleep Vibes is designed to suffuse sensory channels with calm sensations. The senses utilized by this Somniant Technique are those of hearing and touch. These modalities tap a rich vein of pleasurable emotions. The sense of hearing releases our response to music, to voices, to birds, and to flowing water. The tactile sense possesses a primary ability to confer comfort. The infant is lulled by touch in the form of body contact. To the adult, touch in the form of a handshake conveys friendship; in sensual contact, touch stimulates gratification.

Both senses, tactile and auditory, bear a basic relationship to sleep. Mothers instinctively sing lullabies to their babies. A young child in a crib will murmur or croon itself to sleep, often while engaging in rhythmic brushing of the fingertips as sleep approaches.

Sleep Vibes imparts the soothing sensations inherent in sound and touch.

> Lie on your bed in a comfortable position.
>
> Close your eyes.
>
> Clasp your hands lightly over your waist with the fingers interlaced.
>
> Visualize the keyboard of a piano.
>
> Move the fingers of your right hand as if you were depressing five of the keys very gently. As you do so, exhale and hum softly in a barely audible voice. Your vocal cords will vibrate slightly. At the same time, think the word *vibes.*
>
> Pause.
>
> Repeat with the fingers of your left hand, humming and thinking the word *vibes,* as you exhale.
>
> Pause.
>
> Continue the sequence until you feel drowsy. The gentle finger pressure and soft humming will produce a sedative effect.

Saturation Breathing I

Saturation breathing consists of three separate techniques, three slightly different methods of producing drowsiness. Each of the techniques should be practiced for an entire week before you proceed to the next one. At the end of the third week, you may wish to use some or all of them, in combination with each other, or in combination with other techniques.

The goal of saturation breathing is the increase of the carbon dioxide level in the blood. In this Somniant Technique, a series of rhythmic breaths serves as a prelude to breath-holding. As the breath is held, carbon dioxide accumulates and effects a subtle shift in body chemistry. Anxiety is dulled and drowsiness ensues.

The consequences of carbon dioxide buildup have been noted with regard to pilots who must breathe from the limited air supply of their plane's cabin. When reserves of environmental oxygen diminish, carbon dioxide levels rise. The effects upon the pilot include loss in alertness, lethargy, and finally sleepiness. These conditions, to be assiduously avoided at the controls of a plane, are highly desirable in bed.

Saturation breathing draws upon the natural reserves of carbon dioxide in your body. The technique is directed toward achievement of presleep body chemistry through a controlled exercise of normal processes. The procedure is entirely safe. It is not possible to harm yourself by holding your breath. A natural reflex insures that you inhale long before you approach a danger point. The build-up of carbon dioxide in the body is a signal which forces you to resume breathing normally.

You are going to breathe rhythmically, slowly, and deeply, and then you will hold your breath for as long as you can. Each time you inhale, fill your lungs with air and then pause. Each time you exhale, empty your lungs of the last breath of air. Before you get into bed, open a window slightly so that your bedroom is well ventilated. Lie in bed on your back. Now slowly—

1. Inhale . . . Exhale
2. Inhale . . . Exhale
3. Inhale . . . Exhale
4. Inhale . . . Exhale

Your lungs are now empty. With your lungs still empty, hold your breath for as prolonged a period as possible. As you reach the discomfort level, you may notice an odd sensation in your head. When you feel discomfort—

1. Inhale . . . Exhale
2. Inhale . . . Exhale
3. Inhale . . . Exhale
4. Inhale . . . Exhale

With your lungs empty again, hold your breath for as long a time as possible and then—

1. Inhale . . . Exhale
2. Inhale . . . Exhale
3. Inhale . . . Exhale
4. Inhale . . . Exhale

Hold your breath, lungs empty, for as long a time as possible and then—
1. Inhale . . . Exhale
2. Inhale . . . Exhale
3. Inhale . . . Exhale
4. Inhale . . . Exhale

This time, do not hold your breath. Breathe naturally. You should find yourself slightly fatigued. In a few moments, repeat all four cycles a second time, then a third time, and finally a fourth time. You will feel tired at this point. Breathe naturally. You will soon drift off to sleep.

Saturation Breathing II

This technique substitutes sixteen shallow breaths for breath-holding. In all other respects, the exercise is the same as *Saturation Breathing I.* Four cycles are repeated four times, thus:
1. Inhale . . . Exhale
2. Inhale . . . Exhale
3. Inhale . . . Exhale
4. Inhale . . . Exhale

Now take sixteen shallow, quick breaths. Try to inhale as little air as possible. An inhalation plus an exhalation comprises one breath. After the sixteenth exhalation—
1. Inhale . . . Exhale
2. Inhale . . . Exhale
3. Inhale . . . Exhale
4. Inhale . . . Exhale

Again take sixteen shallow, quick breaths. Then—
1. Inhale . . . Exhale
2. Inhale . . . Exhale
3. Inhale . . . Exhale
4. Inhale . . . Exhale

Take sixteen shallow, quick breaths. Then—
1. Inhale . . . Exhale
2. Inhale . . . Exhale
3. Inhale . . . Exhale
4. Inhale . . . Exhale

Breathe naturally. Your anxiety will have lifted. You will soon drift off to sleep.

Saturation Breathing III

This variation is comprised of sixteen deep, slow, saturation breaths, followed by twenty-four quick, shallow breaths. This cycle of deep breaths, followed by shallow breaths, is repeated for a total of four times as in *Saturation Breathing I and II.*

Take sixteen deep, slow, breaths. Each time you inhale, fill your lungs with air and then pause. Each time you exhale, empty your lungs of the last breath of air. Slowly—

1. Inhale . . . Exhale
2. Inhale . . . Exhale
3. Inhale . . . Exhale
4. Inhale . . . Exhale
5. Inhale . . . Exhale
6. Inhale . . . Exhale
7. Inhale . . . Exhale
8. Inhale . . . Exhale
9. Inhale . . . Exhale
10. Inhale . . . Exhale
11. Inhale . . . Exhale
12. Inhale . . . Exhale
13. Inhale . . . Exhale
14. Inhale . . . Exhale
15. Inhale . . . Exhale
16. Inhale . . . Exhale

Now take twenty-four quick, shallow breaths. Repeat the series of sixteen deep breaths and twenty-four shallow breaths three more times for a total of four times. A pleasant sensation of drowsiness will precede your gentle descent into sleep.

Appendix

This section presents Food-for-Sleep Lists indicating the tryptophan, carbohydrate, and fat content of various foods. The information is taken from publications of the United States Department of Agriculture. For additional comprehensive information, we recommend the well-organized and clearly presented reference work *Food Values of Portions Commonly Used* by Bowes, Church, and Church, published by Lippincott. With regard to your diet, you will obtain best results by planning your sleep food in advance rather than with a hit-or-miss approach. While a rigid diet is unnecessary, a sensible eating plan will assist you to improve your sleep.

A. Food-for-Sleep Lists

Four food lists have been prepared:
1. Foods high in tryptophan
2. Foods high in carbohydrates
3. Fruits and their carbohydrate content
4. Foods high in fat

The above lists should be used in the following manner:
1. Foods high in tryptophan should be taken as often as possible throughout the day.
2. Foods high in carbohydrates should be taken two to four hours before bedtime for initardia (inability to fall asleep) and immediately before bedtime for other forms of insomnia.

3. As a substitute for the carbohydrate list (2), above, combine any fruit on list 3, and preferably the higher carbohydrate fruits, with any of the high-fat foods on list 4. Here, too, the foods should be taken two to four hours before bedtime for initardia and immediately before bedtime for other insomnias.

Foods High in Tryptophan

Food	Quantity	Tryptophan (mg) *
Dairy Products		
CHEESE		
Camembert	one ounce	69
Cheddar	one ounce	98
Cottage, creamed	½ cup	168
Cottage, not creamed	6 tbsp.	187
Gruyère	one ounce	105
American	one ounce	91
Swiss	one ounce	100
SOUR CREAM	one cup	94
BUTTERMILK		
From whole	one cup	89
From skim	one cup	96
MILK		
Whole	one cup	120
Skim	one cup	124
EGGS, CHICKEN		
Large	one	112
Medium	one	99
Small	one	83
Meats		
BEEF		
Pot roast	½ pound raw	319
Brisket	¼ pound raw	201

Club steak	½ pound raw	278
Dried or chipped	two thin slices	113
Hamburger,	¼ pound raw	255
Extra lean	¼ pound raw	303
Liver,	3½ ounces	296
Porterhouse	½ pound raw	297
Rib roast	½ pound raw	332
Round, bottom	½ pound raw	474
Round, top	½ pound raw	504
Sirloin	½ pound raw	373
T–Bone	½ pound raw	281
HAM, fresh	3½ ounces	427
LAMB		
Chop	½ pound raw	379
Loin chop	¼ pound raw	162
PORK		
Loin chop	3½ ounces	382
VEAL		
Steak	3½ ounces	389
Breast	3½ ounces	365
Cutlet	3½ ounces	435
Loin chop	½ pound raw	362
Rib chop	3½ ounces	362
Nuts		
Cashew	6 to 8 nuts	64
Mixed	8 to 12 nuts	71
Peanuts,		
Roasted with skin	one tbsp. nuts	50
Roasted without skin	one tbsp. nuts	55

* Tryptophan values taken from publications of the United States Department of Agriculture.

Note: One thousand milligrams (mg) equals one gram (gm).

Foods High in Carbohydrates

Food	Quantity	Carbohydrates (gm) *
BROWNIE	one (2x2x3¾″)	15.3
CAKE		
Angel	1/10 ave. cake	27.1
Chocolate	one piece (2x3x2″)	23.4
Fruitcake	one slice (3x3x½″)	23.9
Plain cake	one serving	22.4
Pound cake	one slice (3x3x½″)	16.4
ECLAIR, Custard	one ave. chocolate icing	39.1
GINGERBREAD	one small piece (2x2x2″)	26.9
ICE CREAM		
Chocolate	1/6 quart	22.2
Strawberry	1/6 quart	21.2
Vanilla	1/6 quart	20.1
ICE MILK, Chocolate	1/6 quart	20.2
JELL-O	one serving (5 per pkg.)	15.1
With whipped cream	one tbsp. cream	16.4
PIE		
Apple	1/6 of 9″ pie	61.0
Banana custard	1/6 of 9″ pie	49.2
Blackberry	1/6 of 9″ pie	55.0
Blueberry	1/6 of 9″ pie	56.0
Cherry	1/6 of 9″ pie	61.5
Chocolate chiffon	1/6 of 9″ pie	70.0
Custard	1/6 of 9″ pie	35.1
Lemon chiffon	1/6 of 9″ pie, crumb crust	46.9
Peach	1/6 of 9″ pie	63.0
Pecan	1/6 of 9″ pie	82.0

Carbohydrate Content of Fruits

Fruit	Quantity	Carbo-hy-drates (gm) *
APPLE, Raw	3" diameter	33.4
APPLE, Baked	with 2 tbsp. sugar	45.7
APRICOTS, Raw	2 to 3 medium	12.8
BANANA	1 large	44.4
CHERRIES, Sweet, raw	15 large or 25 small	17.4
DATES	10 medium	72.9
FIGS, Fresh, raw	2 large	20.3
FIGS, Dried	5 medium	69.1
GRAPES	22 medium	15.7
GRAPEFRUIT	½ (4" diameter)	10.8
MANGO, Raw	1 medium	33.6
NECTARINES, Raw	2 medium	17.1
ORANGE	1 large (3x3" dia.)	28.7
PEAR	1 (3x2" dia.)	30.6
PINEAPPLE, Raw, diced	¾ cup	13.7
PLUMS	2 medium	17.8
PRUNES, Dehydrated	4 medium	47.1
RAISINS	¼ cup	27.5
RASPBERRIES, Frozen	½ cup, sugar added	30.3
TANGERINE, Raw	1 large or 2 small	11.6
WATERMELON, Slice	(6" diameter x 1½")	38.4

* Carbohydrate values taken from publications of the United States Department of Agriculture.

Note: Fruit should be eaten in combination with a food high in fat content for most effective results.

Foods High in Fat

Food	Quantity	Fat (gm) *
CHEESE		
Camembert	one ounce	6.9
Cheddar	one ounce	9.1
Cottage, creamed	½ cup	4.7
Cream	2 tbsp.	10.6
Gruyère	one ounce	8.9
Swiss	one ounce	7.8
COCONUT		
Fresh	one piece (2x1x3/8")	10.4
Fresh, shredded	¼ cup	8.2
Dried, shredded	2 tbsp.	5.9
CREAM		
Sour	¼ cup	10.8
Whipping, medium	one ounce	9.4
Whipping, heavy	one tbsp.	5.6
ICE CREAM		
Regular, 12% Fat	⅙ quart	11.2
Rich, 16% Fat	⅙ quart	14.5
MAYONNAISE	one tbsp.	11.2
NUTS		
Hickory	15 nuts, small	10.1
Macadamia	6 nuts, roasted	11.7
Mixed	8 to 12 nuts	8.9
Pecans	12 halves or 2 tbsp. chopped	11.0
Walnuts	8 to 10 halves or 2 tbsps. chopped	8.7
PEANUT BUTTER	one tbsp.	7.2

* Fat values taken from publications of the United States Department of Agriculture.

Note: Fat should be eaten in combination with a food high in carbohydrates such as fruit for most effective results.

B. *Sleep Clinics*

A list of members of the Association of Sleep Disorders Centers follows. The list does not include institutions where sleep disorders medicine is practised but which are not affiliated with the Association. The listed clinics differ in acceptance procedures. Some accept patients only through referral from a physician; others see patients on a self-referral basis. A preliminary letter or telephone call for this information will speed the referral process.

Arkansas

Sleep Laboratory
Department of Anatomy
Univ. of Arkansas
 Med. Center
Little Rock, AR 72201
Attn: Edgar Lucas, Ph.D.
(501) 661-5272

California

Sleep Disorders Center
U.C. Irvine Medical Center
101 City Drive South
Orange, CA 92688
Attn: Jon Sassin, M.D.
(714) 634-5777

Sleep Disorders Center
1260 15th Street, Suite 1402
Santa Monica, CA 90404
Attn: John Beck, M.D.
(213) 451-3270

Sleep Disorders Program
Stanford University
 Med. Center
Stanford, CA 94305
Attn: Laughton Miles, M.D.
(415) 497-7458

Florida

Sleep Disorders Center
Mt. Sinai Medical Center
4300 Alton Road
Miami Beach, FL 33140
Attn: Marvin Sackner, M.D.
(305) 674-2385

Illinois

Sleep Disorders Center
Suite 214 Wesley Pavilion
Northwestern Univ. Med. Center
Chicago, IL 60611
Attn: John Cayaffa, M.D.
(312) 649-8649

Sleep Disorders Center
Rush-Presbyterian-St. Luke's
1753 W. Congress Parkway
Chicago, IL 60612
Attn: Rosalind Cartwright, Ph.D.
(312) 942-5000

Louisiana

Sleep Disorders Center
Psychiatry and Neurology
Tulane Medical School
New Orleans, LA 70118
Attn: John Goethe, M.D.
(504) 588-5236

Maryland

Sleep Disorders Center
Baltimore City Hospital
Baltimore, MD 21224
Attn: Richard Allen, M.D.
(301) 396-5859

Massachusetts

Sleep Disorders Clinic
Boston Children's Hospital
300 Longwood Avenue
Boston, MA 02115
Attn: Myron Belfer, M.D.
(617) 734-6000

Sleep Laboratory
Department of Neurology
Univ. of Mass. Med. Center
Worcester, MA 01605
Attn: Sheldon Kapen, M.D.
(617) 856-3081

Michigan

Sleep Disorders Center
Henry Ford Hospital
2799 W. Grand Blvd.
Detroit, MI 48202
Attn: Thomas Roth, Ph.D.
(313) 876-2233

Minnesota

Sleep Disorders Center
Neurology Department
Hennepin Co. Med. Center
Minneapolis, MN 55415
Attn: Milton Ettinger, M.D.
(612) 347-2121

New Hampshire

Sleep Disorders Clinic
Department of Psychiatry
Dartmouth Medical School
Hanover, NH 03755
Attn: Peter Hauri, Ph.D.
(603) 646-2213

New Jersey

Sleep Disorders Center
Med. Sciences Building
New Jersey Med. School
Newark, NJ 07103
Attn: James Minard, Ph.D.
(201) 456-4300

New York

Sleep-Wake Disorders Center
Montefiore Hospital
111 E. 210th Street
Bronx, NY 10467
Attn: Charles Pollak, M.D.
(212) 920-4841/3

Sleep Laboratory
Department of Psychiatry
SUNY at Stony Brook
Stony Brook, NY 11794
Attn: Merrill M. Mitler, Ph.D.
(516) 444-2069

Ohio

Sleep Disorders Center
Cincinnati General Hospital
Cincinnati, OH 45267
Attn: Milton Kramer, M.D.
(513) 861-3100

Sleep Disorders Center
Psychiatry Department
St. Luke's Hospital
Cleveland, OH 44118
Attn: Joel Steinberg, M.D.
(216) 368-7000

Sleep Disorders Center
Mt. Sinai Hospital
University Circle
Cleveland, OH 44106
Attn: Herbert Weiss, M.D.
(216) 795-6000, Ext. 531

Sleep Clinic
Department of Psychiatry
Ohio State University
Columbus, OH 43210
Attn: Helmut Schmidt, M.D.
(614) 422-5982

Oklahoma

Sleep Disorders Center
Presbyterian Hospital
Oklahoma City, OK 73104
Attn: William Orr, Ph.D.
(405) 272-9876

Pennsylvania

Sleep Disorders Center
Western Psychiatric Institute
3811 O'Hara Street
Pittsburgh, PA 15261
Attn: David Kupfer, M.D.
(412) 624-2246

Sleep Disorders Center
Division of Neurology
Crozer Chester Med. Center
Upland Chester, PA 19013
Attn: Calvin Stafford, M.D.
(215) 874-9611

Tennessee

BMH Sleep Disorders Center
Baptist Memorial Hospital
Memphis, TN 38146
Attn: Helio Lemmi, M.D.
(901) 522-5651

Texas

Sleep Clinic
Baylor College of Medicine
Houston, TX 77030
Attn: Ismet Karacan, M.D.
(713) 790-4886

Canada

Sleep Laboratory
Ottawa General Hospital
43 Bruyère, Ottawa, Ontario
KIN 4C8, CANADA
Attn: Roger Broughton, M.D.
(613) 231-4738

Sleep Disorders Clinic
Hôpital du Sacre-Coeur
5400 ouest, Boul. Gouin
Montreal, Qu., CANADA
H4J 1C5
Attn: Jacques Montplaisir, M.D.
(514) 333-2070

Bibliography

Antrobus, J. *Discrimination of EEG sleep stages I REM vs. II.* 1965. Association for the Psychophysiological Study of Sleep. Washington, D.C.

Antrobus, J.S., Antrobus, J., & Fischer, C. 1965. Discrimination of dreaming and non-dreaming sleep. *Archives of General Psychiatry* 12: 395-401.

Bond, R.J., & Lader, M.H. 1973. The residual effects of flurazepam. *Psychopharmacologia* 32: 223-235.

Bowes, Church, F.C., & Church, H.N. 1975. *Food values of portions commonly used.* Philadelphia, New York & Toronto: J.B. Lippincott.

Cartwright, R.D. 1974. The influence of a conscious wish on dreams: A methodological study of dream meaning and function. *Journal of Abnormal Psychology* 83(4): 387-393.

Chase, M.H., ed. 1972. *The sleeping brain. Perspectives in the brain sciences.* (Vol. 1). Los Angeles: Brain Information Service. Brain Research Institute, University of Calif.

Cooper, J.R., ed. 1977. *Sedative-hypnotic drugs: Risks and benefits.* Rockville, Md.: U.S. Department of Health, Education, and Welfare. National Institute on Drug Abuse.

Dawson-Butterworth, K. 1975. The chemopsychotherapeutics of geriatric sedation. *Journal of the American Geriatrics Society* 18: 97-114.

Dement, W.C. 1976. *Some must watch while some must sleep.* San Francisco: The Portable Stanford Series. San Francisco Book Company.

Dement, W.C., Carskadon, M.A., Guilleminault, M.D., & Zarcone, V.P. 1976. Narcolepsy: Diagnosis and treatment. *Primary Care* 3(3): 609-623.

Foulkes, D. 1966. *The psychology of sleep.* New York: Charles Scribner's Sons.

Goodman, L.S. & Gilman, A. 1970. *The pharmacological basis of therapeutics.* (4th ed.) London: Macmillan.

Greenblatt, D.J., Allen, M.D., & Shader, R.I. 1977. Toxicity of high-dose flurazepam in the elderly. *Clinical Pharmacology and Therapeutics* 21: 355-361.

Guidelines for the clinical evaluation of hypnotic drugs. Washington, D.C.: Health, Education, and Welfare Publication No. (F.D.A.) 78-3051, September 1977.

Guilleminault, C., & Dement, W.C. 1974. Pathologies of excessive sleep. In *Advances in sleep research.* (Vol. 1) E.D. Weitzman (Ed.). New York: Spectrum Publications.

Guilleminault, C., Eldridge, F.L., & Dement, W.C. 1973. Insomnia with sleep apnea: A new syndrome. *Science* 181: 586-588.

Guilleminault, C., Eldridge, F.L., Simmons, F.B., & Dement, W.C. 1975. Sleep apnea syndrome. Can it induce hemodynamic changes? *Western Journal of Medicine* 123: 7-16.

Guilleminault, C., Eldridge, F.L., Simmons, F.B., & Dement, W.C. 1976. Sleep apnea in eight children. *Pediatrics* 58(1): 23-30.

Guilleminault, C., Peraita, R., Souquet, M., & Dement, W.C. 1975. Apneas during sleep in infants: Possible relationship with sudden infant death syndrome. *Science* 190(4215): 677-679.

Guilleminault, C., Tilkian, A., & Dement, W.C. 1976. The sleep apnea syndromes. *Annual Review of Medicine* 27: 465-484.

Gunby, P. 1978. Medical News. *Journal of the American Medical Association* 239(24): pp. 2529; 2531-2541.

Gunby, P. 1978. Medical news. *Journal of the American Medical Association* 239(25): 2635-2646.

Hall, C.S., & Van de Castle, R.L. 1966. *The content analysis of dreams.* New York: Appleton-Century-Crofts.

Hartman, E. 1973. *The functions of sleep.* New Haven & London: Yale University Press.

Hartman, E. 1977. L-tryptophan: A rational hypnotic with clinical potential. *American Journal of Psychiatry* 34(4): 366-370.

Hartman, E., & Cravens, J. 1977. The effects of long term administration of psychotropic drugs on human sleep: I. Methodology on the effects of placebo. II. The effects of reserpine. III. The effects of amitriptyline. IV. The effects of chlorpromazine. V. The effects of chloral hydrate. VI. The effects of chlordazepoxide. *Psychopharmacologia* (Berl.) 33: pp. 156-167; 169-183; 185-245.

Hecht, A. 1976. *Panel reports on sleep aids.* F.D.A. Consumer. Publication No. (F.D.A.) 76-3012. Washington, D.C.: U.S. Department of Health, Education, and Welfare.

Hobson, J.A. 1969. Sleep: Biochemical aspects. *New England Journal of Medicine* 281(26): 1468-1470.

Jaffee, J. 1977. Hypnotic and sedative agents. In *Psychopharmacology in the practice of medicine,* M. Jarvik, ed. New York: Appleton-Century-Crofts.

Jacobson, A., Kales, J.D., & Kales, A. 1968. Clinical and electrophysiological correlates of sleep disorders in children. In *Sleep physiology and pathology: A symposium,* A. Kales, ed. Philadelphia & Toronto: Lippincott.

Jacobson, Edmund. 1938. *You can sleep well.* Chicago, Whittlesey House.

Jouvet, M. 1968. Insomnia and decrease of cerebral 5-hydroxytryptamine after destruction of the raphe system in the cat. *Advances in Pharmacology* 68: 265-279.

Kales, A., Allen, C., Scharf, M.B., & Kales, J.D. 1970. Hypnotic drugs and their effectiveness. All-night EEG studies of insomnia subjects. *Archives of General Psychiatry* 23: 226-232.

Kales, A., Bixler, E.O., Kales, J.D., & Scharf, M.B. 1977. Comparative effectiveness of nine hypnotic drugs: Sleep laboratory studies. *Journal of Clinical Pharmacology* 17(4): 207-213.

Kales, A., Bixler, E.O., Scharf, M.B., & Kales, J.D. 1976. Sleep laboratory studies of flurazepam: A model for evaluating hypnotic drugs. *Clinical Pharmacology and Therapeutics* 19: 576-583.

Kales, A., Bixler, E., Tan, T.L., Scharf, M.B., & Kales, J.D. 1974. Chronic hypnotic drug use: Ineffectiveness, drug withdrawal insomnia, and dependence. *Journal of the American Medical Association* 227(5): 513-517.

Kales, A. & Kales, J. 1970. Evaluation, diagnosis, and treatment of clinical conditions related to sleep. *Journal of the American Medical Association* 213(13): 2229-2235.

Kales, A., & Kales, J.D. 1975. Shortcomings in the evaluation of hypnotic drugs. *New England Journal of Medicine.* 293: 826-827.

Kales, A., Kales, J.D., Bixler, E.O. 1974. Insomnia: An approach to management and treatment. *Psychiatric Annuals.*

Kales, A., Kales, J.D., Bixler, E.O., & Scharf, M.B. 1975. Effectiveness of hypnotic drugs with prolonged use: Flurazepam and pentobarbitol. *Clinical Pharmacology and Therapeutics* 18: 356-363.

Kelly, Charles. 1961. *The natural way to healthful sleep.* New York: Hawthorne.

Luce, G.G., & Segal, J. 1966. *Sleep.* New York: Coward-McCann.

Meyers, F.H., Jawetz, E., & Goldfein, A. 1976. *Review of medical pharmacology.* (5th ed.) Los Altos, Calif.: Lange Medical Publications.

Morgan, C.T. 1965. Recurrent nervous circuits. *Physiological psychology.* (3rd ed.) New York: McGraw-Hill.

Morgane, P.J., & Stern, W.C. 1975. The role of serotonin and norepinephrine in sleep-walking activities. *National Institute of Drug Abuse Research, Monograph Series* 37-61.

Mulholland, T.B., & Evans, C.R. 1965. An unexpected artifact in the human electroencephalogram concerning the alpha rhythm and the orientation of the eyes. *Nature* 207: 36-37.

Mullan, S., & Penfield, W. 1959. Illusions of comparative interpretation and emotion. *American Medical Association Archives of Neurology and Psychiatry* 81: 269-283.

Over-the-counter nighttime sleep-aid and stimulant products. Tentative final orders. Part II. Washington, D.C.: Federal Register, F.D.A. Department of Health, Education, and Welfare, June 13, 1978, 25544-25602.

Penfield, W. 1959. The Interpretative Cortex. *Science* 129: 1719-1725.

Penfield, W., & Perot, P. 1963. The brain's record of auditory and visual experience. A final summary and discussion. *Brain* 86(4): 595-694.

Rechtschaffen, A., & Dement, W.C. 1968. Narcolepsy and hypersomnia. In *Sleep physiology and pathology: A symposium,* A. Kales, ed. Philadelphia & Toronto: Lippincott.

Rechtschaffen, A., & Monroe, L.J. 1968. Laboratory studies of insomnia. In *Sleep physiology and pathology: A symposium,* A. Kales, ed. Philadelphia & Toronto: Lippincott.

Rifkin, A., Quitkin, F., & Klein, D.M. 1976. Withdrawal reaction to diazepam: Letter to the editor. *Journal of the American Medical Association* 236(19): 2178-2179.

Shapiro, B., & Spitz, H. 1976. Problems in the differential diagnosis of narcolepsy versus schizophrenia. *American Journal of Psychiatry* 133 (11): 1321-1323.

Snyder, F. 1970. The phenomenology of dreaming. In *The psychoanalytic implications of the physiological studies in dreams,* L. Madow & H. Lawrence, (eds.) Springfield, Ill.: Charles C Thomas.

Taylor, C.I., & Miller, W.C. 1976. Narcolepsy: A case report. *Journal of the South Carolina Medical Association* 72: 431-432.

Webb, W.B. 1975. *Sleep, the gentle tyrant.* Englewood Cliffs, N.J.: Prentice-Hall.

Wenger, M.A., Bagchi, B.K., & Anand, B.K. 1961. Experiments in India on "voluntary" control of the heart and pulse. *Circulation* 24: 1319-1325.

Wolf, S. 1959. The pharmacology of placebos. *Pharmacological Review* 11: 689-704.

Wurtman, R.J., & Fernstrom, J.D. (Eds.) 1974. Control of brain serotonin by the diet. In *Advances in neurology* (Vol. 5) S. McDowell & A. Barbeau (eds.). New York: Raven Press.

Wyatt, R.J., Engleman, K., Kupfer, D., Fram, D., Sjoerdsma, A., & Snyder, F. 1970. Effects of L-tryptophan (a natural sedative) on human sleep. *Lancet* 2(678): 842-846.

Wyatt, R.J., Zarcone, V., Engleman, K., Dement, W.C., Snyder, F., & Sjoerdsma, A. 1971. Effects of 5-hydroxytryptophan on the sleep of normal human subjects. *Electroencephalography and Clinical Neurophysiology* 30: 505-509.

Wykert, J. Why sleeping pills are keeping you awake. *New York,* May 24, 1976, 33-38.

Zung, W.W.K., & Wilson, W.P. 1961. Response to auditory stimulation in dream sleep. *Archives of General Psychiatry* 4: 548-552.

Index

L-tryptophan, 31, 172, 173, 174
Latent content, 102, 103
Librium, 163
Life expectancy, relation of sleep to, 9
Light sleep, 14, 23, 24, 28, 55, 64, 65, 69
   wakefulness vs., 29, 61, 68 *See also*
   Hyperlixia
Liquid consumption, 72
Long sleepers, 44, 45, 49
Luminal, 153, 161

Manifest content, 102, 103
Maslow, Abraham, 20
Mattresses, 17
McGill University, 105-6
Medication, 111, 114, 117, 126, 151-
   169
Memories, 107, 108
Meprobomate, 153, 162
Meprospan, 153, 154
Meprotabs, 162
Metabolism, 77
Methapyrilene, 160
Methaqualone, 154, 162
Methaqualone hydrochloride, 154
Methyprylon, 153, 162
Milpath, 153
Milpram, 153
Miltown, 153, 163
Mini-jet-lag, 11, 27
Mistakes made by Somniquest partici-
   pants, 15-17
Morgan, Professor, 45
Mors, 119
Motivation, 48, 181-82
Multisomnia, 13
   description of, 15
Musial, Stan, 41
Myoclonic spasm, 58
Mythology, 119

Naps, 11, 54, 69, 72, 88, 111, 114, 135,
   177
   infant, 74
   middle-age, 74-75
Narcolepsy, 136-39, 150
Nardil, 162
National Cancer Institute, 160
National Institute on Drug Abuse, 154,
   166
Nebralin Tablets, 153

Nembutal, 153, 154
Nervous system, 27-28, 120
   effects of depressants on, 164, 165
   lethal depression of, 163
Neurosis, 103
New England Journal of Medicine, 152
Night terrors, 62, 147, 149-50
Nightmares, 15, 64, 91-92, 94, 96, 98,
   100, 101, 102, 108-9, 110, 111,
   112, 113, 114, 126, 149, 150, 162,
   186, 192
Noctec, 154, 162, 163
Noise, effect of, 11
Noludar, 153, 162, 163
Nonbarbiturates, 154, 155, 163
Nonprescription sleep remedies, 160

Object constancy, 125
Oedipal fantasies, 98
Over-the-counter (OTC) sleep re-
   medies, 160, 161, 167, 169
Oversedation, 165
Oversleeping, 69
Overweight, 145, 147

Pansomnia, 13
   description of, 15
Paraldehyde, 163
Parest, 154
Passionflower extract, 161
Pavlov, A., 20
Pavor nocturnus, 62, 149 *See also* Night
   terrors
Penfield, Wilder, 105, 106, 107, 108
Penobarbital, 153, 154
Pentobarbital sodium, 153
Personality, insomniac, 18-19, 45
Pharaoh, 95-96
Phenobarbital, 153
Pills, 21, 47, 125, 126, 147, 151, 152,
   153, 154, 155, 156, 159, 161, 167,
   168, 171, 186
Placebo, 29, 172, 173
Placidyl, 117, 154, 157, 159, 160, 163
Pleisomnia, 10, 13, 16, 73-90, 172, 176
   description of, 14
Plutarch, 119
Poor sleep, 110
Poor sleepers, 15, 23, 27, 33, 76
Potassium bromide, 160